Instructor's Manual

to accompany

Environmental Economics:
An Introduction

Third Edition

Barry C. Field
University of Massachusetts

Martha K. Field
Greenfield Community College

McGraw-Hill Irwin

Boston   Burr Ridge, IL   Dubuque, IA   Madison, WI   New York   San Francisco   St. Louis
Bangkok   Bogotá   Caracas   Kuala Lumpur   Lisbon   London   Madrid   Mexico City
Milan   Montreal   New Delhi   Santiago   Seoul   Singapore   Sydney   Taipei   Toronto

McGraw-Hill Higher Education

A Division of The McGraw-Hill Companies

Instructor's Manual to accompany
Environmental Economics: An Introduction
Barry Field and Martha Field

2 3 4 5 6 7 8 9 0 QSR/QSR 0 9 8 7 6 5 4 3 2

ISBN 0-07-242922-4

www.mhhe.com

Table of Contents

Preface

Environmental Economics, An Introduction is designed as a text for a one-semester course. It is based on a course I have taught for many years, a course predicated on the notion that the subject is interesting and important enough to be presented to a wide audience of lower-division students, rather than delayed until students have negotiated a set of prerequisite courses. Thus, the book is meant to be used by students *who have not necessarily had any economics yet.* Nevertheless, the book is intended to have a distinctly analytical perspective. Given these objectives it's necessary to focus on a limited number of primary concepts—incentives, efficiency, the equimarginal principle, cost effectiveness, etc. It's also necessary, in the later chapters on domestic and international environmental policy, to concentrate on the main stories, and avoid getting drawn into the endless details that these subjects contain.

After the first two introductory chapters, there are two chapters on the most basic of economic principles. These are probably about the minimum for someone who has never had any economics. In writing these chapters there was a continuing temptation to go for a slightly higher level of sophistication. I tried very hard to resist this, to keep clearly in mind the type of student for whom the book is primarily intended. I would hope that students who have had, say, introductory micro, would find these chapters a useful review.

In this instructor's manual I have worked through each of the chapters, discussing: (a) the objectives of each, (b) main ideas covered, (c) points of discussion (cautions, techniques I have found useful, possible extensions, etc.), and (d) brief answers to each of the questions for further discussion.

The book is 21 chapters long, perhaps too long for students to get through completely under normal circumstances. The book is divided into sections so that different instructors can emphasize the material they find most useful. After having gone through Sections I and II, you may wish to pick and choose chapters from the other sections depending on the relative emphasis you wish to put on: (a) benefit-cost analysis, (b) policy analysis, (c) U.S. environmental policy, and (d) international issues.

The questions at the end of the chapters are called "discussion" questions, but they are perhaps more specific than this label implies. For the most part, they are not meant to lead to open-ended discussion, but have answers which I hope are more-or-less correct. They are designed to lead students toward making modest extensions of the ideas covered, which should help them both review the material and perhaps think more deeply about it.

I have used a number of newspaper articles and other exhibits to illustrate points in the text. The objective is to show students that the economic ideas we are discussing in the classroom are actually at work in the real world.

The entries in the "selected readings" of each chapter are not meant to be exhaustive by any means. Their purpose is to provide students with a few keys, or levers, into the literature, should they want to pursue the topics further, e.g., in writing term papers. So my criterion for including items was primarily to have a wide-ranging set of entries, including books, journal articles, government publications, and so on. In the interests of having material that is accessible to students, few of the journal articles cited are drawn from the more sophisticated side of the environmental economics literature. This may have had the unintended effect of reducing some citations of economists whose work is important in the field. No doubt I have missed some valuable references; let me register both an apology and a request that you point out to me any particular references you think should be included in subsequent editions.

In producing this instructor's manual I want to give special thanks to Martha K. Field for helpful editorial advice, and to Darleen Slysz and Eileen Keegan for their fine production work.

Preface to the Second Edition

The second edition preserves the structure of the first, all the chapters remaining essentially intact. I have rearranged some material, taken some out, and added some new topics. Almost all of the exhibit material has been updated. I have also added a number of examples designed to illustrate important points. Some of the new material is: the environment as an economic and social asset (Chapter 2); regulatory impact analysis (Chapter 6); risk analysis (Chapter 6); the envirotech industry (Chapter 8); environmental justice (Chapter 9); common vs. statutory law (Chapter 10); progress under the tradeable permit program in the 1990 Clean Air Act (Chapter 16); and the economics of recycling (Chapter 17).

The structure of this instructor's manual of course follows the structure of the previous edition. I have tried to add additional material primarily in the sections on "teaching ideas." Most of these come from feedback from both students and other teachers who have used the book. To all of them I am most grateful. Thanks especially to Peggy Cialek for seeing the manual through its revision.

Preface to the Third Edition

The third edition again preserves the basic structure of the book. Some of the new material we have included is: global warming (Chapter 20), brown fields (Chapter 17), the TMDL approach to water pollution control (Chapter 14), and the SO_2 and NO_x trading programs (Chapter 15). The third edition has new discussion questions and exhibits. At the end of each chapter several relevant web sites are shown. Additionally, there is now a web site associated with the book (www.mcgraw-hill.com/economics/field/EE3). On the site additional relevant web sites are referenced.

Thanks again to Eileen and Darleen in preparing the instructor's manual.

Chapter 1

WHAT IS ENVIRONMENTAL ECONOMICS?

Objectives

The purpose of this chapter is to whet students' appetites, by presenting them with some examples of the types of problems environmental economists work on and some of the approaches they take. Most of the examples are illustrated with short newspaper clippings to increase their immediacy. They are meant to be sketches that are easily understandable by students, without the need of devoting a lot of class time to their deeper interpretation.

Main Points

At this juncture there are just two leading ideas to stress: (a) the critical role of incentives in producing environmental degradation and in designing environmental policies, and (b) the importance of studying the short- and long-run benefits and costs of environmental improvements.

Teaching Ideas

It is especially important to set a positive tone early. Most students will come to the class as environmental advocates. With its attention to costs, tradeoffs, and notions of efficiency, environmental economics can seem to many to lead toward a weakening of the forces of environmental advocacy and to lower aspiration levels for environmental improvements. That is why many environmental advocacy groups look on environmental economics with jaundiced eye. It's important to begin getting the message across that this is incorrect, that, instead, the subject will prove to be very useful in such things as designing environmental policies with more teeth than some of those we have had in the past, getting more environmental improvement from the resources we devote to these programs, and learning more about the real levels of environmental damages and the values people put on improving the natural environment.

Many students will also come to the class with the simplistic notion that environmental deterioration is primarily a result of "capitalism," where decisions are presumably made with reference only to the bottom line, and not to wider social or ecological concerns. The collapse of the former socialist countries, and the nasty environmental conditions this has revealed, makes it easy to combat this notion. So does the fact that some of our worst environmental problems in market economies stem from cases where the profit-motive is not

1

at work (e.g., pollution from weapons manufacturing sites). The essential message is that environmental pollution will occur in any system if the incentive system is not structured appropriately.

Answers to Discussion Questions

We have not included discussion questions for this first chapter.

Chapter 2

THE ECONOMY AND THE ENVIRONMENT

Objectives

This is also an introductory chapter, the primary aim of which is to provide a simple conceptualization of the economy in relation to the natural environment, and to establish some definitions and perspectives that will be used throughout the book.

Main Points

A leading idea presented in the chapter is the *materials/energy balance relationship*; it helps to establish the basic relations between economy and environment, and locates some of the major "pressure points" for developing environmental policy. Since the book is limited to environmental economics, the chapter also contains a very brief discussion of issues in *natural resource economics;* the close relationship between the two needs to be emphasized.

The materials balance model does not focus on the handling of residuals at the end of production/consumption, so Figure 2-3 is meant to shift emphasis to this part of the problem. It is also useful for bringing up the major problem of control: when two or more sources contribute to a pollution problem, how much should we control each source?

You may wish to postpone the discussion of production possibility curves until later. The ideas of short-run vs. long-run may be presented fairly intuitively without the diagram, and students who have had no economics may be put off at this stage if you take simple ideas and make them technically complex. Whether you present this material at this point will depend on where you wish to place emphasis in the course. The idea of sustainability is presented here, with a simple interpretation in terms of impacts on future production possibilities curves.

Finally, the material on expenditures for pollution control is to get students thinking about the idea of the optimal, or efficient, level. For many students this will be a new idea, and it is useful at this point to pose the problem but not try to answer it. Discussion question 6 asks students to begin thinking about the factors that go into determining the "appropriate" levels of expenditures.

3

Teaching Ideas

This chapter is bound to have a "grab-bag" flavor, because it includes a variety of topics which, in the nature of things, have no underlying theme. There is probably no way around this; some basic terminology and perspective are essential.

Answers to Discussion Questions

1. Investment in new physical capital, infrastructure or otherwise, creates a difference between M and $(R_p{}^d + R_c{}^d)$; as long as long-lived physical capital is accumulating some portion of the material, inputs will be incorporated in this capital rather than ending up back in the environment. Ultimately (and this may take a long time) everything that goes in will come out.

2. A pollutant is a residual that causes damage. Thus, a residual that is emitted into the environment but causes no damage is not a pollutant. An airborne pollutant, if it were emitted downwind from anything that could potentially be damaged, would not be a pollutant. The same principle applies to noise and junked automobiles. It would be difficult for an ugly building not to lead to damage, as this would imply that nobody views it; of course, when aesthetics are involved the issue of damage is much more problematic than when classic damaging emissions are involved.

3. A short-lived, non-cumulative pollutant does its damage and then disappears, so if we want to reduce damages we need only reduce current emission levels. But a cumulative pollutant stays around to cause damages in the future, so foresight is needed to manage damages, and that is usually difficult to get. It's hard because the science becomes more difficult—having to predict effects that are a long time in the future, and it's hard because people ordinarily discount the future.

4. People often implicitly think of damages as something that causes physical dislocation or impacts on humans or nonhuman organisms. But in a wider sense damages include any alterations in the natural environment that go against the preferences of humans. In the next chapter we will expand on this notion of damages.

5. A very brief and, at this point, intuitive foray into the idea of social efficiency. The optimal level of expenditures depends on preferences, the costs of control technology, and assimilative capacity of the environment of the political entity in question. In my honors section I often ask students to give me two pages on this type of question during the first week of classes. Near the end of the semester I ask them again to give me two pages on this or a closely related question. Most students are astounded at how far their thinking has evolved during the term.

Chapter 3

BENEFITS AND COSTS, SUPPLY AND DEMAND

Objectives

In this and the next chapter the objective is to present a capsule summary of some basic economic principles. Given the space limitations and the intended audience, it has obviously been necessary to keep the story extremely simple. All concepts are in static terms; for example, there is nothing about making decisions over time. The objective of this chapter is to develop the notions of aggregate demand and aggregate marginal cost/supply, so that they can be used in the next chapter on markets, and provide the basis for the standard pollution-control model using marginal damages and marginal abatement costs.

Main Points

The chapter opens with *willingness to pay* because that is an intuitive way of getting at the idea of preferences without having to introduce utility as such. It then moves to demand, individual and aggregate, and finally benefits. The equating of benefits with willingness to pay (or perhaps the more palatable "willingness to sacrifice") is always good for a lively discussion, as one would expect. So is the notion of using a monetary scale to measure willingness to pay.

On the cost side, after a brief discussion of the concept of opportunity costs, I introduce marginal costs directly. It seems just as intuitive to do it this way rather than work through total and average costs in order to get to marginal costs. Marginal cost is tied into technology because technological change in pollution control is given major emphasis in subsequent chapters. Another concept stressed in later chapters is the "equimarginal principle." This is a slight misappropriation of this term because things are being equated at the margins throughout the system, including by consumers. But I think the principle of cost minimization, or output maximization, is sufficiently important in environmental policy that it needs a name of its own.

Teaching Ideas

An effective way of exploring the concept of demand/willingness to pay is to talk about energy conservation. There are two ways to get a reduction in energy use: (1) convince people to use less energy at current prices and (2) drive up the price of energy. Economists naturally focus on the second, because it takes utility functions as given. But environmental advocates will want to emphasize the first also, because efforts to shift these utility functions are just as legitimate to them as simply changing relative prices.

It is important to mention the distributional assumptions underlying the aggregate demand/unwillingness-to-pay function. Willingness to pay in part reflects ability to pay, and redistributions of wealth will produce shifts in the aggregate relationships.

The discussion of aggregate demand is for a private good; demand for public goods is deferred to the next chapter. However, it might be useful, after talking about Figure 3-3, to bring up "environmental quality" as a good, and get students starting to reason on an intuitive basis why the present analysis may not exactly fit that case.

The fact that marginal cost is presented directly rather than via total and average cost makes it important to discuss with students how one can figure out total costs simply from marginal cost curves. In subsequent chapters the analysis will hinge on their knowing how to do this, so it's important to spend enough time at this point explaining it and asking questions such as, "What is the total cost of the increase in output from a to b in the following diagram?"

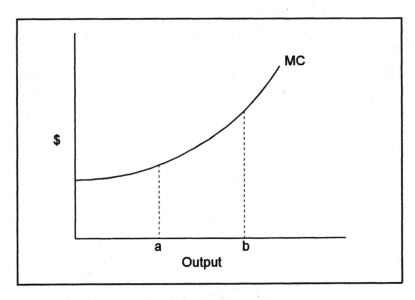

This figure is also used in Question 5 of this chapter.

As many of you know from teaching introductory economics, students often have a hard time relating to the abstract stories told by the graphs. They are not used to thinking about holding the rest of the world constant while they work out the relationship between just a couple of variables. Their intuition is right, because in the real world these two-by-two relationships can get swamped by lots of other factors. I don't know any magic way of giving them this perspective, other than to keep harping on the distinction between positive and normative economics, and trying to convince them that both require these building blocks of seemingly abstract principles and relationships.

The book does not introduce formally the notion of price (or income) elasticity of demand. This was a judgement call; certainly it represents an obvious extension, depending on the students. I felt it would add a layer of technical complexity to the discussion without having a significant yield in terms of student understanding at this level. Another extension is the demand for an input by a firm.

Answers to Discussion Questions

1. The statement "I like clean air more than you do" is interpreted as "I am willing to pay (sacrifice) more for additional clean air more than you are." Note that this could be because we truly have different tastes and preferences, or because we have similar tastes and preferences but I am currently exposed to dirtier air than you are.

2. The good in question is a private good, so the aggregate demand curve is found simply by summing the individual quantities demanded.

Price	Aggregate Demand
10	5
9	8
8	11
7	15
6	19
5	24
4	31
3	40
2	55
1	87

3. A basic advantage of using willingness to pay as a measure of value is that it renders "value" observable and operational; another is that in searching for value it refers to those individuals who are experiencing the good or service in question, i.e., it treats consumers themselves as the legitimate source of judgement as to the value of things. Disadvantages of using wtp are well-known, e.g., that it does not account for differences in wealth between individuals, that it cannot work well if consumers do not know potential outcomes with reasonable accuracy, and that it is subject to intertemporal instability for any number of reasons.

7

Alternatives might include referring to the judgements of scientists or policy makers (i.e., politicians).

4. An aggregate supply curve under competitive conditions implies an equimarginal condition in terms of the distribution of total output among the various firms. Competition minimizes the total costs of producing a given output by dividing it among firms in such a way as to equalize marginal costs.

5. The marginal cost curve would presumably look something like the following:

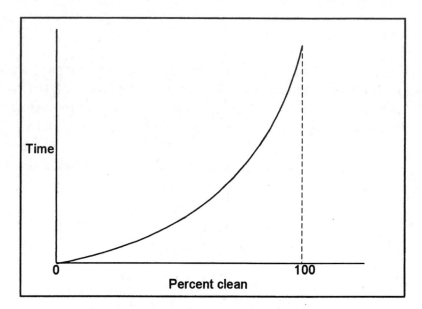

6. A new machine that helps clean rooms would lower the marginal cost of so doing, which would shift the cost curve downward. It's not clear if the curve would ever hit the vertical dashed line at 100 percent clean; is it possible to have a room that is absolutely clean down to the last grain of dust?

Chapter 4

ECONOMIC EFFICIENCY AND MARKETS

Objectives

The aim of this chapter is to present the basic market model, discuss its efficiency properties, then consider what happens in the face of external costs and external benefits. It establishes the basis for the next chapter, having to do with public environmental policy.

Main Points

Certainly a leading point is *economic efficiency*, that state of affairs that pertains when the marginal benefits of some course of action equal its marginal costs. The approach is to identify this output level by reference to society's marginal willingness-to-pay and marginal cost curves, as shown in Figure 4-1. You should stress that these two curves are assumed to capture all of the effects of the given output, wherever and among whomever they occur. Then in Figure 4-2 a market model for this good is presented and we ask the question: Under what circumstances will the *market equilibrium* quantity of this output equal the socially efficient rate previously identified? This opens up the way to discuss external costs, which affect the marginal cost/supply side; and external benefits, which affect the marginal willingness-to-pay/demand side of the analysis.

The discussion of external costs is straightforward. I have used some numbers developed by Rick Freeman to illustrate externalities, in this case stemming from electric power production (see Example 4-1).

The direct type of external costs—for instance a pulp mill damaging a downwind community with airborne emissions—are reasonably easy to understand. There is also a section on open-access resources and the externalities that result. I use the example of a road open to use by anyone. This is not an environmental resource, but I find it instructive because it is intuitive to students. It also has a straightforward metric with which to measure the extent of the externality: increased travel time.

Finally, the chapter contains a discussion of external benefits, focusing on public goods. In cases of external benefits the market left to itself will normally undersupply the good in question. It's then reasonably easy to connect this to improved environmental quality as a public good.

9

Teaching Ideas

Many beginning students, especially if they come from an environmental advocacy point of view, will not see the need of worrying about whether the market is or is not efficient. To them environmental quality is obviously degraded, and that calls for action now. Students in environmental sciences frequently have the idea that policy springs directly from the results of natural and physical scientists. They often believe that it is enough to identify cases of environmental damage and the scientific linkages behind them; remedial intervention will then be obvious. Worrying about the market may strike them as trying to achieve things by working within the system—and shouldn't we be trying to change the system? The answer to these concerns is, presumably, to stress the strength of market forces (witness the ex-socialist countries) and the idea that by making sure that these forces are channeled correctly we can be more effective than any alternative approach.

I have stressed the presence of free riding in public goods because that reflects my personal outlook about how the world actually works. It is true that many people will be driven by conscience to contribute without coercion. There is a substantial literature on "voluntary" forbearance from taking advantage (e.g., tit-for-tat solutions to prisoners' dilemmas). No doubt a minimal level of such behavior is essential for basic social stability. But in large-number cases, and even in many small-number cases where strangers are involved, free riding seems to me to be ubiquitous; hence, I have stressed it.

Answers to Discussion Questions

1. With a marginal cost of $4, marginal cost and marginal willingness to pay would intersect at a quantity of 24 units.

2. This is a question involving a public good (the water quality of the lake). Thus, to find the aggregate MWTP curve we must add individual marginal willingness to pay at different DO levels.

DO Level	Marginal WTP			Aggregate MWTP
	A	B	C	
0	10	10	?	?
1	6	8	10	24
2	4	6	8	18
3	2	4	6	12
4	0	2	4	6
5	0	0	2	2
6	0	0	0	0

10

If marginal costs are $12, the socially efficient level of oxygen in the lake is 3 ppm.

3.   If the demand curves are for cantaloupes, we have a private good and we can add quantities.

Cost of Cantaloupes	Aggregate Quantity Demanded
10	1
8	3
6	6
4	9
2	12
0	15

If the cantaloupe price was $12, it looks like no cantaloupes will be sold.

4.   A bus is a public good for everybody inside it, but private for people not on it. A public phone may be made available by a public utility (which may be a private company) but presumably it is a private good because exclusion is possible. A public park is an open-access resource unless exclusion is possible.

5.   The efficient course of action is to clean the lake to 2 ppm. The total cost of this would be $210 ($50 + $65 + $95), so equal shares would mean that each homeowner would contribute $70. For Homeowner C this amount exceeds their total willingness to pay to clean the lake ($65). Thus, equal sharing would leave this one party worse off. The upshot is that though the cleaning of the lake is efficient for the whole society (in terms of maximizing net benefits), it may not necessarily make each individual better off, or it certainly is unlikely to make everyone better off to the same degree. This creates problems for getting everyone to agree on taking collective action: those who will be benefitted greatly will presumably be eager to organize and take action, while those who would not would be reluctant to do so. Note that a more complicated cost sharing scheme could solve the problem, in this case by having Homeowner C pay a smaller share of the cost than the others.

Chapter 5

THE ECONOMICS OF ENVIRONMENTAL QUALITY

Objectives

The aim of this chapter is to translate the economic concepts of the last several chapters into the language of environmental quality, and to set out the basic pollution-control model to be used in analyzing environmental policy.

Main Points

The chapter introduces the concepts of *marginal damages* and *marginal abatement costs*. It then combines them to focus on the notion of efficiency in pollution control and ambient environmental quality. It's probably the key chapter in the book in terms of conceptual matters, and it may be the most difficult to get across to students. What looks like a simple model actually has many subtleties, and there are real problems with choosing how deeply to explore some of these complications. No doubt this will differ from class to class.

Pollution damages are perhaps the most easily understood, so these are covered first, with the introduction of the marginal damage function. In all the diagrams the horizontal scale has emissions, or ambient concentrations, increasing to the right, so marginal damage curves are going to slope upward to the right in general. I like this approach because the origin then has a natural interpretation, though it does mean that if one wants to talk about the demand and supply curves for environmental quality, these are sloped backwards as compared to normal demand and supply curves.

Figure 5-1 shows four representative marginal damage functions, two emissions functions, and two ambient-quality functions. Important points are their slope, their starting point, their relation to total damages, and the shift factors lying behind them. It's also important that students understand the difference between emissions and ambient functions and the disposal decisions and environmental factors linking them. All functions have been drawn generally sloping upward to the right, as is conventional, but you will probably want to discuss other possible shapes linked to plausible real-world examples. This might include an increasing linear total damage function, which yields a constant marginal damage function; a "wipe-out" function, where some species (humans?) are all wiped out with the first tiny drop of a pollutant, and so on.

A good way to motivate the shift to marginal abatement cost functions is to show students only a marginal damage function and ask them to identify the "best" level of emissions or ambient quality. Many will opt for zero, or perhaps the nonzero threshold level if you have given them a function with this characteristic. Why should we have to put up with any damage? Then put the problem in a real context, say SO_2 coming from a group of power plants. Ask them, if I were to give you $5 billion to spend on anything you wanted, would you use it to reduce these particular emissions to zero? They will see quickly that they cannot answer this without also considering how much it could achieve if it were spent on something else, i.e., how much it is going to cost to reduce these particular emissions.

After introducing the minimum marginal abatement cost, one can then identify the efficient level of emissions, or ambient quality. This is clearly a pivotal point. It is critical to discuss the different situations shown in Figure 5-7, especially panel (c), which shows that for some pollutants the efficient level is zero. One must emphasize that at the efficient level of emissions, the total of abatement costs and damage costs are minimized. Discussion question 1 is intended to emphasize this.

The discussion in the text, together with Figure 5-8, contains some simple comparative statics, showing the effects of shifting marginal abatement and marginal damage costs. Students usually have a very hard time differentiating the *efficient* level of emissions from the *actual*, or current, level. It's the difference between positive and normative. For many students "what should be" follows obviously from "what is," and they do not find it easy to make the distinction.

This chapter also introduces the idea of *enforcement costs*, a topic not adequately treated in many policy discussions. Figure 5-9 shows a very simple analysis, in which enforcement costs act like standard abatement costs. This has the unfortunate implication that the full socially efficient level of emissions is higher than when abatement costs only are considered, but opens up new possibilities for pollution control via improvements in enforcement technology and institutions.

Finally, this chapter has a short, very explicit explanation of the "equimarginal" principle. As you have no doubt gathered by now, this is one leading idea I try to get across to students during the course. As mentioned earlier in the chapter, minimum aggregate marginal abatement costs require that the equimarginal principle be satisfied across the sources involved in the analysis.

Teaching Ideas

There are many subtle points lying behind the apparently simple ideas of marginal damage and marginal abatement costs. Many students are likely to be skeptical that all damages can be measured in monetary terms. This may be true of damages inflicted on human beings, but what about damages to an ecosystem that cannot be linked directly to humans? Even many human damages are elusive. One can take the "innocent" approach: We have to have a metric so we will use money, faute de mieux. Or the hardline approach:

13

In fact, we are making great strides in measuring damages in monetary terms, as we will see in the next few chapters. Or something in between: We still have a long way to go in measuring damages, but meantime we must have a conceptual way, at least, of discussing the problem.

Once having introduced the damage function, one has a means of talking about the relationship between the economic and ethical approach to environmental improvement. In the short run, we take whatever damage function is out there, trying to measure it and designing policies with reference to it. The ethical approach, making people feel a greater sense of the wrongness of environmental destruction, can be interpreted as an attempt to lift the damage function, to move people to a state where they are willing to sacrifice more for environmental protection measures than they were before.

The rising marginal cost of pollution control has a neat little example that will resonate with most students. It's the marginal cost of cleaning their dorm room. The time to do a 30% cleaning job may be quite modest given what we know about the state of the average room. But as the degree of cleanup increases, the time investment is going to increase substantially, and the cost of getting that last 10% will be extremely high. That is, there are rising marginal costs associated with cleaning up the environment.

Answers to Discussion Questions

1. One can take points to the right or left of e* and show diagrammatically that the total social costs in either case would be higher than they are at e*.

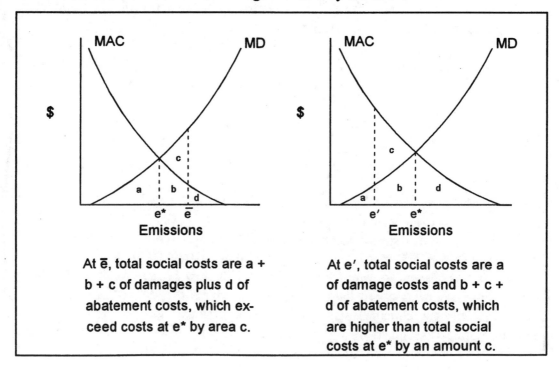

At ē, total social costs are a + b + c of damages plus d of abatement costs, which exceed costs at e* by area c.

At e', total social costs are a of damage costs and b + c + d of abatement costs, which are higher than total social costs at e* by an amount c.

2. The invention would lower the marginal abatement cost function and reduce the *efficient* level of emissions. Whether the *actual* level of emissions was lowered would depend on whether the invention were actually adopted by the pulp mills, and this would probably depend on the pollution-control regulations in effect.

3. In this case the increase in the number of homes would shift the marginal abatement cost function upward. But it probably would shift the marginal damage function upward also, since more people would be living in the vicinity of the lake. The efficient level of water quality would be affected by the relative amounts of the shifts; if they were the same, E* might not change. Whether actual water quality levels changed would presumably depend on what steps new homeowners took to reduce their septic tank emissions; if they follow the same practices as the existing homeowners the actual water quality of the lake would probably go down.

4. With an equiproportionate reduction, each firm would be reduced to 5 tons of emissions. The total costs of doing this for each firm would be:

   Firm 1: $60 (0 + 4 + 8 + 12 + 16 + 20)
   Firm 2: $21 (0 + 1 + 2 + 4 + 6 + 8)
   Firm 3: $15 (0 + 1 + 2 + 3 + 4 + 5)

   Thus, aggregate abatement costs for an equiproportionate reduction would be $96.

   To meet the 15 tons total emissions and satisfy the equimarginal rule we reduce Firm 1 to 8 tons, Firm 2 to 5 tons, and Firm 3 to 2 tons. Total emissions would be 15 tons, and each firm would have marginal abatement costs of $8. Aggregate costs would be $69, calculated from:

   Firm 1: $12 (8 + 4)
   Firm 2: $21 (1 + 2 + 4 + 6 + 8)
   Firm 3: $36 (1 + 2 + 3 + 4 + 5 + 6 + 7 + 8)

   So the cost savings would be $96 - 69 = $27.

5. This gets at the difficulty of managing an episodic type of pollution. Since oil spills are probabilistic, it will take some time before it is known whether the change in navigational rules has indeed shifted the distribution of oil spills. Even if it had, we could easily experience an oil spill next year, but this might not give us very strong evidence that the rule change would not reduce spills in the long run.

Chapter 6

FRAMEWORKS OF ANALYSIS

Objectives

This chapter is the first of three aimed essentially at the question of measuring damage and abatement costs, as introduced in the previous chapter. The primary goal in Chapter 6 is to sketch out some of the different types of policy analysis to which economists contribute, and to present the primary elements of benefit-cost analysis.

Main Points

The chapter contains a brief description of (1) environmental impact analysis, (2) economic impact analysis, (3) cost-effectiveness analysis, (4) damage assessment, and (5) risk analysis. It has a longer discussion of benefit-cost analysis, in which are covered the following points:

(1) **Basic Framework.** I have tried to put this in the context of the pollution-control model introduced in the previous chapter, rather than the facility-type analysis (dams, etc.) which is often used. Thus, Figure 6-1, which discusses the difference between the net-benefits criterion and the benefit-cost ratio, is an emission reduction model in which e_1 represents no program, and "output" consists of varying degrees of emission reduction.

(2) **Discounting.** The discussion covers the mechanics of discounting, the problem of what discount rate to use, and the effects of different discount rates on program decisions. Among environmental advocates it is pretty standard to believe that we should not discount the future heavily, maybe even using a zero rate of discount. The fear is that a high discount will lead us towards undervaluing potential large-scale future environmental impacts. It's important to point out that low discount rates can also have unfortunate effects. In the 1950s and 1960s, federal dam-building agencies sought to expand their budgets by using low discount rates, so they could accumulate enough distant-future benefits to overcome high initial construction costs. The discount rate controversy comes up again in Chapter 19 in the discussion of policy choice in developing countries.

(3) **Distributional Issues.** The discussion focuses mostly on establishing the terminology: regressive, proportional, progressive. I have not gone into exactly

how distributional issues should be handled, except to say that we need to be more aware of how benefits and costs are distributed.

(4) **Uncertainty.** This section presents the idea that many outcomes are probabilistic, and introduces the concept of expected values and attitudes toward risk.

Teaching Ideas

Instructors may differ with respect to whether they wish to cover this section in sequence, or perhaps skip it now and come back to it after pursuing policy issues. When the marginal abatement cost and marginal damage functions are presented as in Chapter 5, there are obviously two main lines of inquiry that it points to: the measurement problem—how do we know where the functions are in any particular case of environmental pollution; and the policy problem—how do we move from situations of too much pollution to a level that is efficient. In my own teaching I find that it flows more easily to move into the policy analysis, so I skip the material in Chapters 6, 7, and 8 for now, go directly to the material in Sections IV and V, and then come back to benefit-cost analysis nearer the end of the course. In doing this I have to deal with those students to whom the measurement issues loom large, telling them that, for now, they will have to trust me that we have developed techniques to measure damages, to which we will turn later. Other instructors will want to cover measurement issues directly at this point, and can simply use these chapters in the sequence followed by the book.

Answers to Discussion Questions

1. An economic analysis of this regulation would look at its impact on such things as car prices and the numbers and types of cars sold, employment effects in California and elsewhere, and so on. A cost-effectiveness analysis would look at the cost of this regulation in relation to the quantity of emissions reduced (so many million dollars per 100 tons of mobile source emissions reduced). A full benefit-cost analysis would look both at the costs of the regulation but also its benefits in terms of reduced damages that would be forthcoming from it.

2. Developing an entirely new engine would probably have much larger development costs than developing add-ons to existing engines. Thus, a decision to develop the new engine would require a longer-run perspective in which distant future benefits would be counted on to outweigh the up-front costs. A high discount rate would reduce the weight of these future benefits, and thus reduce the relative attractiveness of the new engine option. So lowering the discount rate would increase the attractiveness of this option relative to the add-on option.

3.   Calculating net benefits and the b/c ratio at different emission rates gives:

Emission	Net Benefits	b/c Ratio
10	0	0.0
9	2	2.0
8	4	2.0
7	12	3.0
6	23	3.6
5	30	3.1
4	33	2.6
3	26	1.7
2	20	1.4
1	8	1.1
0	-12	0.7

Net benefits are largest at emissions of 4 tons per month, while the b/c ratio is highest at 6 tons per month. Decreasing emissions will increase net benefits as long as the marginal change in benefits exceeds the marginal change in costs. But the b/c ratio could go either way, depending on the absolute amounts of benefits and costs.

4.   Present value of costs: $80/.04 = $2,000. At a discount rate of .04, the present value of benefits is $1,602, while at a discount rate of .02 the present value of benefits is $4,358. So at .04 the net benefits are -$398 while for .02 they are $2,358. Since the benefits are delayed in time relative to costs (benefits bump up to $150 per year, but only after the 50th year), net benefits are clearly higher when the discount rate is lower.

5.   The perceptions that people have about which risks are the most significant often differ from those that scientific studies show to be most significant. Thus, people may be willing to pay to reduce risks that scientists show to be relatively insignificant or, conversely, not willing to pay very much to reduce risks that scientists show to be high. The logic of willingness to pay would seem to imply that it is people's perceptions, not scientific studies, that should rule. But perceptions are affected by all sorts of things, including the way the information about different types of risk is "packaged" and made available to people. If one could make the case that people don't understand the relative risk of different courses of action, and that they would behave differently if they did, one could presumably justify setting policy on scientists' risk estimates rather than individuals' risk perceptions.

Chapter 7

BENEFIT-COST ANALYSIS: BENEFITS

Objectives

In this chapter the main objective is to show students how environmental economists have approached the problem of measuring damages stemming from environmental degradation. This is the benefit side, because reducing emissions or ambient concentrations confers benefits in the form of reduced damages. As the text says, the attempt is to establish the logic of the approaches and review the main techniques, without going into great detail. Many students will be skeptical that we can actually get reasonably good estimates of the marginal damage function contained in the basic model. A major aim of the chapter is to show them that this is one of the primary directions of study within environmental economics.

Main Points

The chapter begins with a brief review of direct damage estimation, especially as regards health impacts, then shifts to the standard willingness-to-pay perspective. The first job is to establish the logic of the approaches; this is done by describing what are normally called the indirect approaches (averting purchases, hedonic methods, travel costs) and differentiating them from the direct approach, otherwise known as contingent valuation.

On the indirect approach side, most space is devoted to discussing the study of wage differences for what they say about the value of life and health; and house prices for what they say about the value of amenities like clean air. It is important to explain the economics of the capitalization process by which these prices adjust to reflect the values of the underlying characteristics. The role of information in this process is worth stressing.

The effects of pollution on production costs is discussed in this section, using a very simple model of the firm. As a possible extension, a more complicated version, with changing output price, is discussed below. The text discussion of the travel cost method is also very brief, without any analytics. A simple numerical example is presented below for those who might like to go into it more deeply.

The chapter contains a fairly long discussion of contingent valuation, which seems appropriate because of the popularity of this method. The discussion includes something on mechanics—design of the questions; some results that various researchers have obtained; and something on the various problems inherent in the method. The last few pages of the chapter cover some of the general problems of benefit estimation—discounting, willingness to pay vs. willingness to accept, non-use values, and restoration costs as proxies for damages.

Teaching Ideas

Given the vast amount of theoretical and empirical work recently in benefit measurement, this chapter represents just a very brief excursion into the subject. In writing this chapter there was a constant pull to go deeper into the various topics, but I sought to resist this in favor of trying to establish the concepts, together with some of the results. Those who have been actively engaged in this work will no doubt find this frustrating, but the students, at this level, risk being overburdened with details that will obscure the main outlines of the problem.

Many students will question the apparent anthropocentrism of the chapter. Benefit estimation is based on willingness to pay, meaning that there is apparently no way for nonhuman values to get counted. There are various responses to this. Many of the ecosystem changes that might occur as a result of environmental pollution will have long-run impacts on humans, even though they may not appear to at the present time; this argues for taking a long-run perspective in benefit-cost studies. Of course, doing this does not get at the problem of the average person being unable to see, and therefore being willing to pay to avoid, some of these real long-run impacts. This perspective still emphasizes the impacts on humans. A more radical view is that nature has no values, it is only humans who can place relative values on different outcomes; thus, "non-human values" can only be human artifacts from the very beginning, so there is nothing inherently wrong with a human-based approach to benefit estimation.

The example in Figure 7-1 shows a situation where the price of the output is unchanged, for example a relatively small area producing a crop that is widely produced elsewhere. The more complicated case of a downward sloping demand curve might be an appropriate extension for an honors section, or in a class where greater emphasis is put on benefit measurement. Using a presentation similar to Figure 7-1, this situation would be:

20

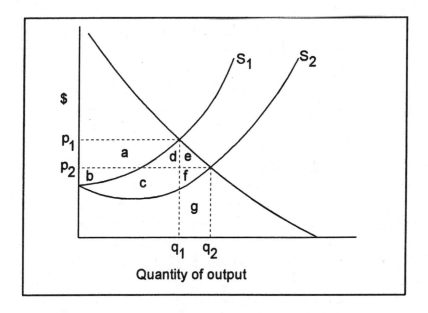

Change in consumer welfare from price reduction: a + d + e
Change in producer welfare: (b + c + f) - (a + b) = c + f - a
Net change: c + d + e + f

I have not used the concept of economic rents or consumers' surplus anywhere in the book. My feeling is that at this level, what one gets in terms of additional understanding is not worth the effort needed to explain these concepts.

There is only a brief discussion of the travel cost approach, laying out the basic idea and then asserting that it is possible this way to estimate a demand function for certain environmental amenities. A longer example is the following. Suppose we focus on the behavior of a single family who lives a given distance away from a free public park. Assume that we have done some survey work and found that this family visits this park an average of four days per year. We then estimate their travel costs to go from their home to the park and return. Assume that cash travel costs—gas, wear and tear on the car, food, etc.—are $18 per trip and that the round trip takes one hour each way. To get the full travel cost we need to put a value on the time spent traveling. This is tricky because what we need is value foregone, in terms of salary or other income, by spending this time traveling rather than working. Empirical work on this has established a value of ⅓ to ½ of the wage rate; for our purposes let us assume their travel time is worth $8.00 per hour. Thus, the total cost of the trip would be $34. This is the price the household pays for each visit to the park.

Now suppose, to keep things very simple, that there are only three other families within range of the park, and that for each of them we have surveyed their travel costs and the number of park visits they make each year. For the four families the travel cost and visit information is the following:

21

	Travel Costs	Park Visits/Year
Family 1	$24	6
Family 2	$34	4
Family 3	$44	2
Family 4	$54	0

Among these families the total visits are 12 per year. In effect we now have the observations that we need to trace out a demand curve for the park: when access fees are set at zero, visitation will be 12 visits per year. Suppose we then imagine that a $10 per day entrance fee is charged at the park. For the first family, the total cost will now be $34 ($24 of travel costs plus the $10 entrance fee). Now we make a critical assumption: that this family's visitation rate will be the same as was the family who paid $34 in travel costs before the change. Thus, the visitation of the second family will fall off to four visits per year. Likewise, the second family will now have a total cost of $44 ($34 of travel cost plus the $10 entrance fee), and we assume their visitation will fall off to two visits per year, i.e., the rate the third family visited before the entrance fee. Meanwhile the total costs of the third family have now risen to $54, and we assume their visitation drops to zero. So, with a $10 access fee, total visitation will now be six visits per year, and we have another point on the total demand curve for the park.

This is the simple mechanics of how we build up an aggregate demand curve for the park using information about the travel costs paid by various visitors to the park. Of course, in practice, it is much more complicated than this. Families will differ in terms of many factors, not just in terms of their travel costs to this park. They will have different income levels, they will differ in terms of the presence of alternative parks and other recreational experiences available to them, and so on. So surveys have to collect large amounts of data on many visitors in order to be able statistically to sort out all these various influences on park visitation rates.

We can now use this approach to estimate the benefits of improving the quality of the environment at the visitation site, for example, by improving the water quality at a recreation lake so that fishing is better. To do this we must collect information not only on recreators and their travel costs to a single recreation site, but to many different sites with differing natural characteristics. Then we can parse out the effects on visitation of various qualitative aspects of different sites. Improving the quality of a site makes that site more desirable in the eyes of recreators and, therefore, shifts the demand curve for the site outward. The accompanying figure shows two demand curves for a lake for recreation purposes, as measured with the travel cost approach. The effect of the cleanup program is to shift the demand function outward, as indicated. Benefits to recreators are measured by the area between the two demand curves, the cross-hatched area in the figure.

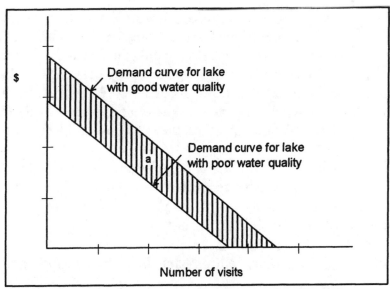

Shift in Demand Curve for a Recreation Lake Brought
About by Improved Water Quality

Answers to Discussion Questions

1. The general approaches one might take are those listed early in the chapter: (1) Look at averting costs, the costs people have experienced to protect themselves from diminished water quality—perhaps water purification, reduced contact, etc. (2) Look at home prices here and at similar lakes to find out how they might respond to increased water quality; use a travel cost approach to place a value on the increased recreational opportunities that improved water quality would make possible. (3) Carry out a contingent valuation survey with a questionnaire designed to elicit willingness-to-pay responses by homeowners for improved water quality.

2. The advantages of using avoided costs for measuring benefits is that it may be relatively easy to estimate some numbers. We have pretty good data on what it costs, e.g., to hospitalize people or treat them if they have various illnesses. Likewise, we have reasonably good data on school costs, though in this case the linkage between expenditures and results is less clear. The main disadvantage is that in actual fact these remedial expenditures may not be made, so the damages of ill health among school children are the reduced capabilities they have in terms of life skills and job skills, and these would be extremely hard to assess.

3. Probably the only way of getting at this would be to carry out a contingent valuation study in which you survey students and ask them about their attitudes to the litter.

4.   Economists are talking about the value of a *statistical life*, not the actual life of some named individual. For example, what are the benefits of putting in a traffic light that will lower the *probability* of accents. Both indirect and direct methods can be used to approach this. Studies of choices people make among risky jobs can be used to reveal the value they place on accidental death probabilities. Of course direct methods could be used as well. Care would have to be taken to be reasonably sure that respondents have an appreciation of the risk situations they will be asked to evaluate.

5.   Students will think of their own ways of phrasing the questions. The important point is how they choose to make respondents aware of the physical significance of improved air quality, perhaps through showing them pictures of differing degrees of visibility associated with different levels of air quality.

6.   This is a student project, which will probably be approached differently by different students.

Chapter 8

BENEFIT-COST ANALYSIS: COSTS

Objectives

Here the goal is to acquaint students with some basic ideas about the cost side of benefit-cost analysis. With all the attention that benefit measurement gets, there may be a tendency to neglect the other side of the analysis.

Main Points

The concept of *opportunity cost* is the first topic covered; since this underlies most of the subsequent points of discussion in the chapter, it is obviously important to get this idea across at the beginning. Additional examples would no doubt be useful, e.g., the costs of paying workers who would otherwise be unemployed, unpaid family labor, etc. There are short sections also on *environmental costs* of environmental programs, primarily through media switches; *no-cost policy changes* that result from rectifying price distortions; and *enforcement costs*.

The rest of the chapter is organized to go from the particular to the general—from costs of a single facility, to costs for a single community, to costs for an industry, and finally to costs to a nation as a whole. Each of these corresponds to an important policy perspective, so this progression seems more relevant than any other. In each section I have tried to give examples that will convey some of the main problems of cost estimation at that level.

The chapter also contains discussions of the important *with/without principle*, and the question of minimum vs. actual (i.e., greater than minimum) costs. Most of the pollution control efforts in the U.S. have not been cost-minimizing ones, for a number of reasons. In retrospect, the chapter may not give adequate attention to the procedures that must be followed to achieve minimum costs. This would include a restatement of the equimarginal principle, as well as an intuitive application to the choice of cost-minimizing input combinations for individual projects and programs.

The chapter contains also a discussion of output adjustments and their relation to the slope of the demand curve (again, I have avoided bringing in the concept of elasticity explicitly). In doing this I have used flat marginal cost curves, so that there is no need to get into the intricacies of industry expansions and contraction. Finally, the chapter includes a short discussion on long-run structural changes and technological change, and the difficulties these create for long-run cost estimation.

Teaching Ideas

A topic that may need more emphasis is the distribution of costs, of a project or environmental control program. Much of the political fighting over environmental policy is, after all, centered on who will bear the cost of cleanup programs. Good illustrations are the hazardous-waste site cleanup program under superfund and the regional distribution of costs under the national acid-rain control program. It would be valuable to discuss various cost allocation principles, such as that costs be allocated in proportion to benefits received, or in proportion to current wealth levels.

Answers to Discussion Questions

1. If one focuses only on the directly impacted industry, that is apparently what it means. But, as we have tried to stress throughout the book, enforcement costs have to be considered. If enforcement costs were to remain unchanged, the implication is true, but with a different regulation they may change, in which case the total costs of the changed standard will be different.

2. The costs would be measured in terms of the development value the land would have that are foregone. If one were to make the assumption that no development will take place as a result of the restriction, then the full value would be a cost. If one assumed that development is diverted to another location, the lost value of development would be the difference in developed values between the protected location and the spot to which development is diverted.

3. As we will see in the next set of chapters, policies differ in terms of the extent to which they encourage technical change in pollution-control activities. Such technical change leads, in general, to lower pollution abatement costs, implying that if we adopt policies that have strong incentives for technological change in pollution control, we can expect to achieve substantial reductions in future abatement costs.

4. The problem here is assuming that the same quantity of gas will be sold even though the price is 10¢ a gallon higher. But a price rise of this amount would lead, other things being equal, to a reduction in quantity demanded, the amount of which depends on the price elasticity of demand. Of course, other things are never equal in the real world, e.g., population growth may occur, which would tend to offset part or all of the price increase.

5. This makes cost estimation for a single industry much more complicated. If all firms were alike, it would be possible simply to take a look at the costs of a representative firm and then multiply the results by the number of firms. If there are a relatively few types of firms in the industry (small vs. large, for example), one could do the same thing

as a weighted average of the number of firms in each category. If the firms are truly all very heterogeneous, one will simply have to either study them all, or make a guesstimate as best as one can.

Chapter 9

CRITERIA FOR
EVALUATING ENVIRONMENTAL POLICIES

Objectives

This is the first chapter in Section IV, dealing with the analysis of environmental policy. Its main goal is to provide the students with some standards by which we can discuss and evaluate the different types of environmental policies covered in subsequent chapters.

Main Points

The chapter discusses five criteria for evaluating public policies. The first is a combination of *efficiency and cost-effectiveness.* Although these are different, putting them together streamlines the list of criteria and highlights the efficiency objective, broadly conceived. At this stage the approach is strictly static: minimum marginal abatement costs and equality between them and marginal damages. Given the discussion of discounting in the last few chapters, it's possible now to get students thinking about these curves as representing present values, but this extension ought not to get in the way of understanding the basic ideas.

The second criterion is *income distribution.* The basic terminology (progressive, regressive, proportional) was introduced in Chapter 6, so if you have jumped to the present chapter directly from Chapter 5, it will be necessary to provide an explanation of these terms here. The concept of "environmental justice" is introduced, but its full discussion is delayed until Chapter 16.

The third criterion is the long-run factor of *technological change,* which for the purposes of the book are wrapped up in the question of lowering the marginal abatement cost function through research and development. It would perhaps be useful to include material on the economics of the pollution-control industry, but the background material for this is not readily available. So what I have tried to do is focus on the effect of policy in providing incentives to reduce marginal abatement costs, without giving much institutional and industrial detail about how that actually happens.

The fourth criterion is *enforceability,* meaning how easy it is to monitor and sanction violators. A large part of the story here is the type of data that have to be collected to enforce (adequately) any particular type of policy.

Lastly, there is a criterion having to do with the apparent *moral dimensions* of public policy; in particular, whether a policy seems to violate accepted moral standards. The text mentions subsidies as a policy that may violate many people's feeling about who should bear the cost of environmental improvement. Slogans like the "polluter pays principle" have the ring of moral rectitude. Often, of course, moral correctness is attached to courses of action with which one has historical familiarity; change, therefore, is often morally suspect, in addition to possibly costing a person something.

Teaching Ideas

There may be other criteria that you wish to discuss, though I have tried to set the ones in the text broadly enough so they will incorporate others as special cases. One possibility, for example, is whether policies incorporate *perverse incentives* that tend to undermine their objectives, but this can presumably be included in the 1st criterion (factors leading away from efficiency), or perhaps the 4th (factors leading to attempts to hide emissions or inflate base-level emission rates, etc.).

Political acceptability is obviously a criterion of importance, but I have not included it in the chapter. This is an extremely slippery factor that I think is best left to political science texts and discussions. What is politically acceptable changes from one time to another, depending critically on the shifting strategic situation and the resources that policy makers are willing and able to spend. While political factors are of obvious importance in the real world, my feeling is that the discussion in the text should focus on economic factors.

Answers to Discussion Questions

1. This is the "fast train to the wrong station" syndrome. Cost effectiveness deals only with the cost side of a policy, asking whether the objective, whatever it may happen to be, is being achieved in a least-cost fashion. Efficiency also requires that the objective meet the criterion of marginal abatement costs = marginal damages. In a standard pollution-control model, any place on the marginal abatement cost function is cost effective for that particular emission or ambient quality level, but only one emission or ambient quality level will be (in general) efficient.

2. This might be interpreted as saying that the net benefits of environmental protection are regressively distributed, accruing more to higher-income people than to lower-income folks.

3. These obviously are complicated issues. As far as mobile-source emission controls, the cost side works primarily through increased automobile prices, and increasing prices always have regressive impacts. One mitigating factor in this case may be that stricter

standards on new cars increase the relative value of used cars, which may advantage poorer people, who presumably are greater owners of older cars. As far as the benefits of mobile-source emission control, one can only say that these would be felt largely in urban/suburban areas, and that this could work to the advantage of lower-income people; if so, the benefits might be progressively distributed. The distribution of net benefits from programs to insure the quality of public water supplies would depend importantly on how the costs were financed, e.g., out of general tax revenues vs. out of user fees. The latter would presumably be more regressive than the former. As for benefits, anybody connected to the water supply would presumably benefit, probably in proportion to the amount of water consumed.

4.   The problem with unenforceable regulations is that they rely strictly on moral means for compliance, and moral capital is probably subject to diminishment when enforcement is absent. One could, however, conceive of situations in which damages from a pollutant or practice are so high that an unenforced regulation is justified.

5.   This is a technology standard. The catalytic converters would presumably have a beneficial effect in the short run. But focusing on this particular technology might divert attention from looking for and developing alternative technology that would be more effective.

Chapter 10

DECENTRALIZED POLICIES: LIABILITY LAWS, PROPERTY RIGHTS, VOLUNTARY ACTION

Objectives

Here the aim is to show how many environmental problems may be handled through decentralized types of institutions, to show the advantages of such procedures in cases where they will work, and to point out their drawbacks, which are important enough in most cases to push people towards policies involving more direct collective efforts.

Main Points

The chapter begins with a discussion of liability laws, then moves to a discussion of property rights. Some may think this backwards, on the grounds that one cannot discuss liability until property rights are specified. But I find the notion of liability so intuitive for students that I prefer to start with it, using it eventually to show that there is a prior issue, which is the distribution of property rights. Students are much more used to the idea of liability than they are to the idea that property rights might be rearranged, which might in turn give different results in terms of environmental quality. There is an excerpt from "A Civil Action" that points out the problem of dealing with scientific uncertainty in the courtroom.

The chapter introduces the concept of transactions costs, the costs of finding, concluding, and enforcing exchanges among individuals and groups. The discussion emphasizes the linkage of transactions costs to the number of people involved and to the difficulties of overcoming public goods and free-rider problems in the case of environmental benefits and costs.

A simple "Coase Theorem" is presented, along with a brief list of requirements that have to be met for decentralized transactions among property owners and users to yield efficient outcomes. The text stresses the lack of a complete set of markets as a real problem with property rights approaches to environmental quality issues.

Finally the chapter discusses *voluntary action* as an approach to pollution control. A major part of voluntary action is based on moral suasion. Moral appeals are frequently undervalued by hard-headed economists, but may be quite effective in some cases, and may be the only realistic approach in others (e.g., littering). Behavior based on morality and feelings of civic virtue is not an either/or proposition, but amenable to change as circumstances change. For example, the same person will behave differently in anonymous situations

31

than in situations where her or his behavior may be easily monitored. The chapter also includes material on the notion of informal community pressure, as it might work, for example, through the toxic release inventory (TRI).

Teaching Ideas

The notion of decentralized solutions to environmental externalities is a concept that many students will have a hard time with. For many of them, as well as for many people in general, externalities almost by definition call for collective action of one type or another. One possible way of backing into this is to start off by discussing the advantages and disadvantages of action at different levels of government. Many environmental impacts are not necessarily federal concerns; because of the nature of the externalities, they can be handled at the state level. By the same reasoning many can best be addressed at the community level rather than the state level. One can then go to the last step and say that many externalities may be handled at the individual or small group levels through negotiations among affected people.

One reason that students have a hard time with decentralized approaches is that one of their major strengths is to resolve something that many students don't see as a particularly big problem. This is the question of identifying the demand/willingness to pay by people for improvements in environmental quality. Most students will come into the course with the view, probably strongly held, that "environmental quality has clearly been seriously degraded, so let's get on with the job of cleaning it up." The idea that it is important to look for efficient points, where marginal abatement costs equal marginal damages, is not something with which they will be immediately impressed. Thus, the strength of the property-rights approach—putting owners and users in direct interaction so they can work out the benefits and costs as they impinge on themselves, and, thus, the most efficient use of a resource, will be less impressive initially to most students than it is to most economists.

The chapter does not contain a discussion of the efficient assignment of property rights/liability, and this would make a good extension for those who would like to spend a little more time on property rights issues. The idea of the welfare-maximizing assignment of property rights is perhaps best approached through a simple example. Here we follow the basic structure of the problem set out by Walters (Stephen J. K. Walters, *Enterprise, Government, and the Public*, McGraw-Hill, 1993, pp. 476-485). An upstream mill is polluting the waters of a river, the damage costs of which are being borne by the residents of a downstream community. These are external costs from the standpoint of the mill. The situation is pictured as follows:

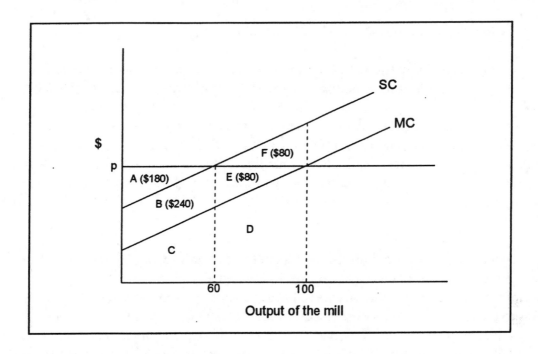

The firm sells its output at the constant price p, MC are marginal private costs of the mill, SC are marginal social costs, including the private costs and the downstream externalities. At an output level of 100, net social benefits are equal to the value of all output minus all costs, or (a + b + c + d + e) - (private costs: c + d) - (external costs: b + e + f) = a - f = \$80. This is the output level that would pertain if the firm were to maximize its net income, without regard to external costs. Assuming zero transactions costs, the socially efficient level of output is \$60 (revenues of a + b + c minus costs of b + c gives a net of \$180), and with costless transactions this is the output level that would pertain, regardless of whether or not we make the mill liable for downstream damages.

But suppose the mill and the community cannot effectively interact, or that the transactions costs of doing so are simply too high. Where should we put the liability? According to Coase it should be put on the party that would have the cheapest means of avoiding the external costs. Suppose the mill could install pollution-control equipment that would alleviate all externalities at a cost of \$100. On the other hand, suppose that the externalities could be alleviated by the community installing water treatment facilities downstream at a cost of \$500. The outcomes would be as follows:

Liability on mill:

Operate at 100 with treatment
Net income: (a + b + c + d + e) - (c + d + 100) = \$400

Operate at 60 without treatment but paying for damages
Net social income: (a + b + c) - (b + c) = \$180

33

Liability not on mill:

Operate at 100 with community spending $500 for water treatment
Net social income: (a + b + c) - costs of water treatment = $100

In this case the property rights assignment that would lead to a maximum of net social income is to make the mill responsible for damages. On the other hand, suppose the mill would require $400 to treat emissions, while the community could treat their water supply for $100. Recalculating these net incomes will show that a maximum can be obtained if the mill is not held liable for damages, leading the community to take steps to avoid the externality.

One possible way of introducing transactions costs into the standard model is to show them as the net result of marginal damage and marginal abatement cost functions. Gains to polluters from reducing emissions are reduced damage costs minus the costs of negotiation. Gains to polluters from increasing emissions are the reduced abatement costs minus the costs of negotiating the increase. Then one could show different equilibria depending on whether the initial situation is one of high or low emission levels. For example, in the following diagram, $\overline{MD}$ is marginal damages minus costs of negotiating decreases in emissions (assumed to be borne entirely by damages), while $\overline{MAC}$ are marginal abatement costs minus costs of negotiating emissions increases (assumed to be borne entirely by polluters). Then starting from e_1, we end up at e_2, while starting from e_0 we end up at e_3. There is an intuitive logic about this, though the graphical modeling of transactions costs may be beyond many students at this level.

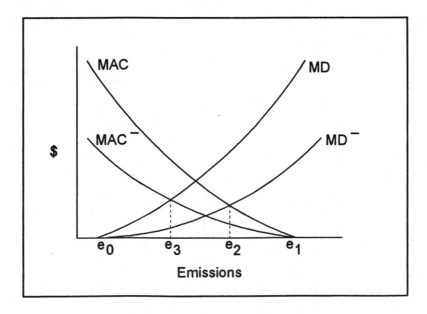

Answers to Discussion Questions

1. Suppose it is left up to each landowner to decide how to use their property. Any landowner could decide, for example, whether to leave her land undeveloped, use it for houses, or perhaps develop it for commercial purposes. Of course each use would create some externalities, impacts on surrounding landowners and community residents. But negotiations could be pursued by the landowner and neighbors, and in cases where the potential externalities were large, the latter could agree to pay the landowner to refrain from development, while in cases where the externalities are not large, this would become apparent during negotiations and development would be pursued. If it were costless, or nearly so, to negotiate, this process would lead to the efficient amount of development. But, of course, a procedure like this would lead to enormous transactions costs on a community-wide basis. It would be far less costly to enact rules collectively on land conversions. While the rules make impossible some land uses that would be efficient individually, in general it manages land use with far fewer resources of time and energy than if each landowner had to bargain with surrounding landowners. The same argument holds if the rights to develop were held by neighbors, which is why communities pass land use control laws and regulations.

2. Changing the burden of proof would vastly change the relative costs of the different participants in courtroom situations. Putting the burden of proof on polluters would substantially increase the costs of not reducing emissions, which would lead to substantially lower emissions, at least until widely acceptable (acceptable to judges) means for showing no damage were developed.

3. Moral suasion would probably be a lot more effective if the data on behaviors is open to all to see. So publishing the waste disposal data would probably lead many people to reduce the waste stream, even with no further inducement.

4. This is difficult to answer. It is probably the only good way of approaching certain problems such as littering, when there are insufficient resources to monitor people's behavior very directly. It may also be quite effective in cases where accurate individual source emission data can be made available publicly. Research is needed on the susceptibility of people to moral arguments for pollution control.

5. Suppose you will be held liable for average damages rather than the actual damages of any spill for which you may be responsible. Thus, you would gain if your spill was actually above average, and you would lose if the damage you caused was below average. So you would have the incentive to use bigger trucks and loads, that is, larger than average. When everybody does this, the average size of load, and average damages, will increase over time. But if all truckers know this is likely to happen over time, would they refrain from going to larger trucks? Probably not, because for any individual trucker, *average* truck and load size is a public good, over which they have

35

no control. As each one tries to take individual advantage of this fact, the average will increase.

Chapter 11

COMMAND-AND-CONTROL STRATEGIES:
THE CASE OF STANDARDS

Objectives

A primary goal of this chapter is to show students that the use of standards, while deceptively simple and apparently straightforward in application, is more difficult to manage and problematic in terms of results than is often thought. The chapter stresses that standards have weaknesses in terms of short- and long-run cost-effectiveness, but that they have advantages in terms of compliance monitoring.

Main Points

The first section simply introduces the three main types of environmental standards—ambient, emissions, and technology (also called design or engineering standards). The rest of the chapter deals with various aspects of the economics of standards. The first issue is the *level of the standard,* discussed in relation to an ambient standard as in Figure 11-1. There are two important facets to this problem. The first is the general one of where to set the standards in relation to marginal benefits and marginal abatement costs. This is, of course, the *balancing issue,* which the students should now have an easy time with because of the earlier material, especially the standard pollution-control model of Chapter 5. This edition has material about the recent case decided by the U.S. Supreme Court on whether EPA has been using appropriate considerations to set ambient air-quality standards.

The second part of the question is the one about whether regulators should set *uniform standards* or not. If standards are to be set in accordance with some notion of marginal abatement costs and marginal damages, this would imply that they should be set at different levels when these circumstances differ. We will run into this many times in later chapters when we discuss the implications of setting uniform standards in heterogeneous economic circumstances.

There is a section on the long-run impacts of standards, especially the questions of the incentives the standards provide for engaging in R&D to reduce marginal abatement costs. Of course, this presents an overly simple image of the pollution-control industry, and class discussion might usefully point out that there is in fact a pollution-control industry that specializes in residents handling equipment and methods. The incentives for innovation on the part of polluters is translated in part to a demand for new products by the pollution-control industry.

37

The other major topic covered in the chapter is *enforcement,* a problem that is not given sufficient weight in many economic analyses, though that seems to be changing. It is important to help sensitize students to the fact that it is necessary explicitly to think about enforcement; that standards, like any laws, have to be enforced. The discussion introduces the distinction between *initial compliance* and *continued compliance.*

Teaching Ideas

Belief in the efficacy of publicly-prescribed standards to bring about changes in behavior is deep in the bones of most students. They are surrounded by standards: speed limits, age limits for alcohol consumption, automobile license requirements, housing codes, etc. They are part of a culture which sees law as basically a matter of setting and enforcing standards, and they usually accept without question the basic idea that, if actual behavior is not conforming to standards, it must be because enforcement is not sufficiently vigorous.

There are perhaps two central messages to get across here. One is to take advantage of the situation and shift the discussion to the economics of enforcement; this will be a new idea for most students and can be a very valuable lesson. The other is that for many situations there are some better alternatives to standards, especially the incentive-based strategies.

It is useful to pursue with students the basic tradeoff question in enforcement—the allocation of resources to enforcement up to the point where their marginal cost is balanced by the marginal gains. This is inherent in Figure 11-5, where enforcement costs have simply been added to standard abatement costs to get what might be called aggregate marginal abatement costs. A more direct way might be to use a graph like the following:

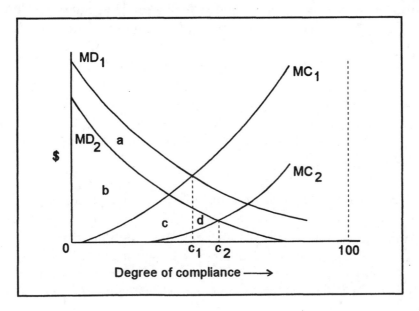

Here the horizontal axis shows degree of compliance, i.e., actual compliance in proportion to theoretically complete compliance. This may be a new idea for many students because they are used to thinking of compliance as binomial, either yes or no. Speaking of compliance in continuous terms will be an innovation. The MC curves show the marginal costs of achieving increased compliance; their location depends on enforcement technology and on the particular standard employed. For example, MC_2 refers to a less stringent standard that sources will have an easier time meeting, and therefore the marginal costs of achieving compliance are lower than for the standard pertinent to MC_1.

The MD functions show the reduction in damages resulting from increased compliance. MD_1 refers to the stricter standard and MD_2 to the less stringent standard. One can then discuss the efficient levels of enforcement and examine the net benefits of enforcement. The case shown in the figure is one where the net benefits of the less stringent standard (the area b + c + d) are possibly higher than those of the more stringent standard (a + b).

Uniform standards are discussed primarily in terms of the equimarginal principle and the added costs they imply when marginal abatement costs differ. I have not stressed enough, perhaps, the savings in implementation costs that uniform standards might entail, relative to policy approaches that treat sources differently. Most of the argument for uniform standards is based on two ideas: equity, through treating everyone alike, and "leveling the economic playing field," through requiring that every source meet the same environmental requirements. When marginal abatement costs differ among sources, however, these two ideas don't necessarily imply equal standards.

There is an ambiguity in the marginal abatement cost concept that good students will identify. Some differences among marginal abatement costs are legitimate and others are not. If you are dealing with sources in two different industries, but emitting a common residual, marginal abatement costs will differ because of different technologies in use. But suppose we are dealing with two firms in the same industry, and that one firm has relatively high marginal abatement costs because it has dragged its feet in adopting new pollution-control technology. Why should this firm be allowed to cut back its emissions relatively less, as it would be by the equimarginal principle?

A point that is perhaps not stressed enough is the perverse incentive that an agency might produce if it sought to set standards so as to equalize marginal abatement costs. This means that firms with lower marginal abatement costs will be required to reduce emissions more than firms with high MACs. This would create a disincentive for firms to search for ways of lowering their abatement costs—just the wrong incentive that we would like to have at work in any environmental policy.

There are political reasons for the popularity of standards, which the text does not go into to any extent. Many environmental advocates are distrustful of the political system, seeing it as being too much subject to manipulation by economically powerful polluter interests. Thus, they are led to reject policy approaches that would give any discretion to policy makers or polluters, thinking that the latter would use these opportunities to weaken the overall rate of cleanup. Standards have the aura of definiteness and of taking discretion out of the hands of polluters and policy makers. Of course, this is not really true, because enforcement efforts are discretionary, but the very fact that the political process is open and subject to influence by whatever groups find it in their interest may push many people to favor a standards approach.

An enforcement issue not discussed in the book, but which makes good classroom discussion, is the private enforcement of environmental statutes. Most federal environmental laws allow private citizens to bring suits against polluters to cover damages caused by pollution or to compel compliance to permit conditions. Citizens may also sue public officials if they believe them to be deficient in carrying out applicable environmental statutes. (A good reference is Wendy Naysnerski and Tom Tietenberg, "Private Enforcement," in T. H. Tietenberg, ed., *Innovation in Environmental Policy, Economic and Legal Aspects of Recent Developments in Environmental Enforcement and Liability*, Edward Elgar, Aldershot, England, 1992, pp. 109-136.) It brings up interesting issues of burden of proof, the public goods aspects of court action, the effect of private enforcement when the policy itself is not cost effective, and so on.

Answers to Discussion Questions

1. The perverse incentive is that this system favors polluters whose emissions were relatively high in past years. The higher the past emissions, the higher the allowable emissions after the percentage cutback. So if there is any inkling by polluters that this type of program might be installed sometime in the future, there is an incentive to keep emissions high so as to have a high base when the cutback is calculated.

2. Standards on the use of an input (e.g., controls on quantities using farm chemicals); standards on operating procedures (e.g., minimum temperatures for incinerators); standards on allowable technologies (e.g., double hulls for oil tankers).

3. With the appropriate areas indicated, the graph is the following:

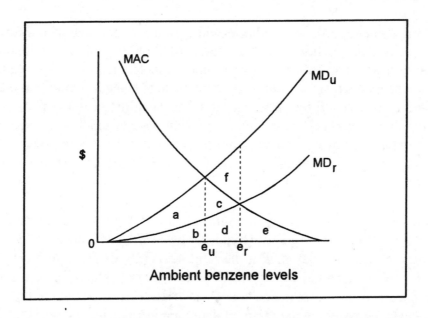

Ambient benzene levels

The social costs are the amount by which the total of abatement costs and damages are above the amount pertaining when rural and urban standards are set differently and efficiently. If the rural standard is set at e_r and the urban one at e_u, then total social costs are $(b + d + e) + (a + b + c + d + e)$. If, instead, the standard is set at e_r for both regions, total costs are $(b + d + e) + (a + b + c + d + e + f)$, for a difference of amount f. If instead the standard was set at e_u for both regions, total cost would be $(b + c + d + e) + (a + b + c + d + e)$, for a difference of amount c.

4.   In graphical terms, cutbacks that involve equal total abatement costs are those in which the relevant areas under the marginal abatement costs (MAC) are equalized, as in the following graph, in which areas a and b are equal:

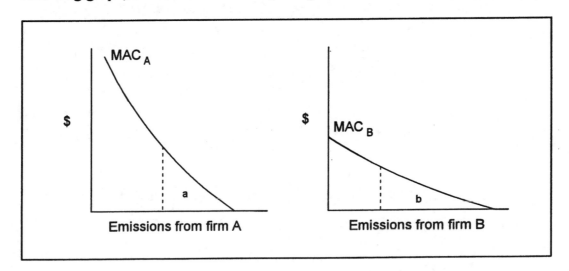

In general, equiproportionate cutbacks will equate neither marginal nor total abatement costs. The equiproportionate cutback standard, though sounding eminently fair, gives no attention at all to differential marginal withholding costs. The equal-total-cost cutback also sounds fair, and does have the virtue of being based to some extent on the MACs of the different firms. The steeper a firm's marginal abatement cost function the less it would get cut back (assuming conventionally-shaped MACs), which is the same result that falls out of the equimarginal cutback. But, in general, they will not be the same, because one case equates the heights on the respective MACs while the other equates the areas under them.

5. The thought is that by enforcing the same emission standards in different countries, it would rule out any one country trying to get a cost advantage in world trade by adopting less strict standards. But the same standards are likely to have different cost effects in different countries. If marginal abatement costs differ, the same standard would increase costs more in one country than another. If we wanted to set standards so that costs increased by the same total amount in all countries, we would have to set them less strictly in countries with high marginal abatement costs and more strictly in countries with low MACs.

Chapter 12

INCENTIVE-BASED STRATEGIES:
EMISSION CHARGES AND SUBSIDIES

Objectives

This is the first of two chapters devoted to incentive-based policies. In this chapter the aim is to explore the way emission charges (taxes) and subsidies work, given the conventional incentives of profit-seeking firms, and to examine the advantages and disadvantages of using charges and subsidies to achieve improvements in environmental quality.

Main Points

The first topic covered is the basic mechanics of how a tax on emissions would work. This is shown in Figure 12-1. It is important for students to see that taxes involve the firms in two types of costs, abatement costs and tax costs, and that firms will try to minimize the total of these. Thus, the firms have the incentive to equate marginal abatement costs and the tax.

There is a brief discussion of emission taxes as a *transfer payment* from the standpoint of society. A point to emphasize is that tax revenues can be used by public authorities to pursue any number of objectives, including encouraging pollution-control activities of the same industries that paid the tax. This is emphasized in Example 12-1. To emphasize the transfer-payment discussion, one can discuss the two-part emissions tax, showing how the amount of the transfer payment can be varied while leaving unchanged its allocative impact on emission reductions.

There is a brief discussion of the thorny problem of how to determine the best rate for the tax. It seems reasonable to discuss this in terms of the rate that will bring about the efficient level of emissions. Finding that level is difficult if we have no good idea of the true marginal damage function. There is a substantial section on emission taxes and the equimarginal principle, since cost-effectiveness is one of the major advantages of the tax approach. The text stresses that a tax will allow us to achieve cost-effective emission controls even though we (i.e., administrators) do not know the marginal abatement costs of each source. (Be warned that clever students may ask: If we don't know the individual marginal abatement costs, we won't know the aggregate marginal abatement cost function, and if we don't know this, how do we have any hope of setting an efficient tax rate?)

There is then a discussion of emission taxes in the case of *nonuniform emissions*, which leads to a discussion of the *zoned emission tax*. Here the emphasis is on the tradeoff between the administrative cost of situations involving multiple tax rates and the costs in terms of lost cost-effectiveness when differently situated sources are nevertheless charged a common emission tax.

There is a discussion of emission taxes and uncertainty, with an attempt to introduce some of the ideas stemming from the "prices vs. quantities" question that was featured in Weitzman's paper (M. Weitzman, "Prices vs. Quantities," *Review of Economic Studies*, Vol. 41, 1974, pp. 447-491). I have discussed only the question of uncertainty about the location of the marginal abatement cost function, and the problems administrators could get into if these functions are relatively elastic.

The next section deals with the long-run effects of taxes on the *incentive to innovate*, and shows the greater incentives that would pertain here, as compared to standards, for firms to try to shift downward their marginal abatement cost functions. Then there follows an important discussion of taxes and *enforcement costs*. The discussion stresses the importance that a tax system places on being able to monitor emissions accurately. This, in turn, motivates a discussion of situations where taxes may be placed on something other than residuals because of monitoring difficulties; a clear example is taxing agricultural chemicals or fertilizers to encourage reduced use and care in application. The discussion stresses the fact that taxes placed elsewhere than directly on the pollutant we desire to reduce can have weak effects.

The section on taxes ends with a discussion of *distributional impacts* of taxes. In competitive industries, output prices will have to increase sufficiently to cover the increase in abatement costs and the tax payments of the firm, which will be more than the cost increases of firms subject to a set of cost-effective emission limitations enforced via standards. The standard conclusions about the regressive effects of price increases are presented. It is worth pointing out that many of the most highly polluting industries are not perfectly competitive (utilities, automobiles, chemicals), so conclusions about how much prices will go up as a result of emission taxes are complex. The section ends with the idea that we might usefully regard emission taxes more as "sin" taxes, like the ones on cigarettes and alcohol that are so often turned to for revenue reasons.

Then comes a discussion of *subsidies*, in which it is shown, via a numerical example, that they have the same allocative effects as taxes at the level of the firm. Finally, the chapter concludes with a discussion of *deposit-refund systems*, where a tax and subsidy are combined on a given product or pollutant.

44

Teaching Ideas

A common reaction from beginning students is that polluters will simply pay the emission tax, pass the burden on to consumers through higher prices, and continue emitting the same quantities as before. This involves explaining the principles of input choice by profit-seeking firms, and applying this reasoning to the question of how firms will respond to higher prices for the services of the environment. In keeping with the level of the book I have not introduced isoquant maps and diagrams of firms responding to input price changes. So the discussion has to proceed on an intuitive basis, starting with a discussion of the cost-minimizing incentives facing profit-seeking firms. A good example is the response of firms and consumers to the increase in energy prices of the 1970s. When the embargo first started, many people thought that firms and consumers would be unable to adjust energy use, because the activity of the economy was so closely tied to energy consumption. But it became abundantly clear that much substitution away from energy was possible as firms and consumers sought to reduce the impacts on them of increased energy prices.

Answers to Discussion Questions

1. Each year motorists would have to have their emissions checked and their mileage recorded. Then emissions could be multiplied by total miles driven to find total emissions, which would then be subject to a tax. One can think of many potential problems: tampering with odometers, getting the car tuned up just before a visit to the emissions check station, collecting emissions taxes on cars that are junked during the year, etc. But the system certainly would have a direct incentive effect, not only to shift to low-emission vehicles, but also to drive fewer miles.

2. If each firm is facing the same emission tax, and each adjusts its emissions so that their marginal abatement costs equal the tax, they will all be operating at the same marginal abatement cost, i.e., the equimarginal rule will be satisfied.

3. There are two parts to the question: will they reduce emissions, and will they pass on the increased costs. Firms, whether competitive or monopolistic, will reduce the use of any input that has gone up in price, and this applies to emissions. But we also expect costs to get passed on in a competitive industry; prices of output will have to go up by an amount sufficient to cover the increased production costs.

4. In industries that are at least reasonably competitive, the ultimate payer of the taxes are consumers of the goods and services produced by these industries. One might argue that price increases are always regressive. Or one might argue that consumers are rightfully the ones who should pay, since they are the ones who are ultimately responsible for production.

5. A two-part emission charge. Also a phase-in period in which charges start low and are gradually increased according to a preannounced schedule.

Chapter 13

INCENTIVE-BASED STRATEGIES:
TRANSFERABLE DISCHARGE PERMITS

Objectives

The aim of this chapter is to acquaint students with the rudiments of transferable discharge permits (TDP) as a cost-effective approach to pollution control. Like the last few chapters, the policy is presented largely from a (simple) conceptual standpoint, so that students may understand the strengths and weaknesses of the approach when we shift in subsequent chapters to studying the economics of controlling particular types of pollutants.

Main Points

The chapter begins with a discussion of *general principles* behind TDP systems: the legal specification of the permits and the way they may be traded; the result of trading, in terms of bringing marginal abatement costs into equality across different sources; and the development of a market for discharge permits with trading among buyers and sellers producing a market price for the permits.

There is a section on the difficult problem of the *initial distribution of rights*. It must be stressed that if the system is to produce significant cleanup, the initial rights must be limited to something below current aggregate emissions. The jaundiced eye with which many people view TDP approaches stems from their belief that public authorities will not be able sufficiently to restrict the total number of permits in circulation.

A brief discussion on *trading rules* tries to stress the fact that permit trading will be very sensitive to rule specification, and that the desire of public agencies to fine-tune the rules and move the market in certain directions will serve to create uncertainty in permit markets and undermine their effectiveness.

Nonuniform emissions are discussed, and it is proposed that zones could be specified, within which permits would transfer one-for-one, while between zones there would be trading ratios to reflect differences among average transfer coefficients of sources in different zones. There follows a discussion of the potential conflict between environmental factors, which may imply restricting the size of trading zones, and economic factors, which suggest larger trading zones so as to foster greater competition.

Enforcement is discussed, with conclusions similar to effluent taxes: one must be able to monitor emissions accurately for the system to be feasible. Additionally, public authorities must be able to keep track of who has the permits—which may be a more difficult problem than it appears in a TDP market with many participants, with banking and temporary leases allowed, periodic adjustments in the "value" of each permit, etc.

Finally, the chapter discusses long-run incentives for R&D and technical changes in pollution control produced by TDP systems, showing that it is the same as for tax programs. The financial flows are a little different, however. A firm subject to an effluent tax can lower its tax liability by adopting less costly abatement methods, while a firm in a TDP system can actually gain some revenues from the sale of permits to help defray the costs of adopting new pollution-control techniques.

Teaching Ideas

This is a relatively short chapter for such a complicated topic. There are innumerable lines of inquiry that could be pursued in discussing further the conceptual basis of TDP programs and their feasibility in particular cases. Since the TDP approach is based on the functioning of markets, it is important to stress the basic principles of market operation and the factors that are critical to their success or failure. There are the standard ones we discuss in principles courses—standardized product, numerous buyers and sellers to foster competition, widespread information, etc. There are more subtle ones that we don't often stress because we take as given the basic institutional background—clear and reasonably stable rules and laws governing trade, expectations that the market will not be subject to excessive political manipulation in the future, etc. Markets for discharge permits are fairly new, however, and regulators are still developing new rules and regulations governing trades. How different rules will affect trades and the efficiency properties of TDP markets is a subject on which more work is needed by economists. As an example see: Robert W. Hahn, "Regulatory Constraints on Environmental Markets," *Journal of Public Economics*, Vol. 42, 1990, pp. 149-175. Hahn examines the effects of several rules through which regulators seek gradually to reduce the number of permits in existence by requiring that for each permit a buyer wishes to obtain, they must purchase more than one permit from current holders.

This is part of the general issue of the ways that public authorities can affect the total number of permits in circulation. Discussing this will deepen students' understanding of how the system is meant to work. It will also get at one of the main problems that environmental advocates have with TDP programs: once the original entitlements have been distributed, authorities will have lost a good deal of control. Authorities could buy permits on the open market, they could expropriate them periodically, or they could retire them through time according to a fixed schedule. Of course, these have major implications for uncertainty in the market and its ability to function efficiently.

I have alluded to some of the fierce political-economic factors that are likely to come into play in TDP markets. All interested parties—polluters, public agencies, environmental groups—are going to want to slant the rules so that the TDP markets work in directions they would most like. Political controversies will be strong over how many permits to create in the first place, how many to be given to various interested parties, and the rules governing their transfer. Conflicts will certainly result over the long-run issue of reducing the number of permits in circulation in order gradually to improve the ambient environment. Although the TDP system has desirable efficiency properties, it is certainly open to as much political manipulation as any of the other approaches to environmental policy, if not to more.

Answers to Discussion Questions

1. Solid waste: establish tradable permits for quantities of solid waste disposed of (something like this is actually happening in some communities). Plastic phaseout: distribute tradable use permits to current users (or producers) of the plastic, then "recall" a certain number of permits each year according to some predetermined phaseout time schedule. Recycled newsprint phase-in: distribute "permits" (in this case we might want to call them something like "unit requirements") requiring each user of newsprint to purchase a certain quantity of recycled newsprint, with the number of "permits" allocated to each newsprint user gradually increasing over time.

2. Firms would adjust their emissions so that their marginal abatement costs equaled the permit price. If there is a single market price for permits, this means that all firms would have the same marginal abatement costs.

3. a. Each source would be cut back to five tons.

   Source A: Total cost = 0 + 2 + 4 + 6 + 8 + 10 = 30
   Source B: Total cost = 0 + 4 + 8 + 14 + 20 + 30 = 76
   Aggregate costs = 30 + 76 = 106

   b. Firm B would buy permits from Firm A, up to the point of equalizing marginal abatement costs. This would be 3 tons for A and 7 tons for B. So A would sell 2 permits to B. Costs would be:

   Source A: 0 + 2 + 4 + 6 + 8 + 10 + 12 + 14 = 56
   Source B: 0 + 4 + 8 + 14 = 26
   Aggregate costs = 26 + 56 = 82

   Note the total cost saving is 106 - 82 = 24. Source A's abatement costs would go up by 26, while Source B's would go down by 50. The permit price negotiated by the two sources would have to lie between these numbers.

c. Suppose you initially gave all the permits to A. Gains from trade still exist, and would lead to the same end point, i.e., 7 tons of emission for A and 3 for B. But now Source A sells 3 permits to B instead of 2, as in the previous case.

4. The pros and cons will probably be different for different groups and market participants, so we should perhaps focus on just trying to predict the impacts that different trading rules would have on the market. If trading is restricted to polluters who are, let's say, the original holders of all permits, it will be relatively easy for rights holders to predict who the suppliers and demanders will be (not in terms of specific firms, but in terms of relevant economic characteristics) in the permit markets. So it will be relatively easy to predict prices and trading patterns, because the market is functioning to redistribute the existing stock of permits among emission sources. Market uncertainty is minimized. With trading opened up to other groups, uncertainty is increased because it's much more difficult to predict how these new participants will behave in the market. Suppose one allows environmental groups to enter the market, on either side. Their offers for permits will reflect their willingness to pay to reduce damages, and this could be high or low depending on what groups are involved, how widely they search for funds to buy permits, etc. The effect of this will be to increase uncertainty in the market, and anything that increases uncertainty will make the market work less smoothly. The same could be said about participation by public agencies and other nonpolluter groups.

Chapter 14

FEDERAL WATER POLLUTION-CONTROL POLICY

Objectives

This is the first of four chapters on U.S. environmental policy. Its primary aim is to identify the main features of federal water-pollution control policy and then to evaluate these features by bringing to bear some of the analytical ideas presented in previous chapters.

Main Points

The chapter starts with some introductory material on the physical and chemical nature of water pollution, focused around a brief discussion of the oxygen sag phenomenon for degradable pollutants in water bodies. It then presents a quick summary of post WWII federal policy toward water pollution, which is summarized in Table 14-1. The rest of the chapter covers essentially three topics: the economics of technology-based emission standards; the municipal wastewater treatment plant subsidy program; and new directions in water pollution-control policy.

There is a relatively long discussion on the establishment of technology-based emission standards. A leading idea is that concepts like "Best Available Technology," or "Best Practicable Technology," incorporate a kind of engineering judgment on whether higher degrees of control are justified by the cost. There is then a section dealing with the question of whether the actual quality of water in the country's rivers and lakes have been improved as a result of this federal effort. Of course, data like those presented in Table 14-4 are interesting but ultimately ambiguous because they are based on before/after analyses, rather than with/without pollution-control programs. This is a good opportunity to emphasize that distinction.

There are sections on the implications of a technology-based effluent standard system for *short-run cost-effectiveness* and for *long-run incentives for technological improvements*. The system performs badly on both of these criteria. Table 14-4 contains some results from a number of studies in which the costs of equiproportionate reductions have been compared to cost-effective reductions.

The section on long-run technological change stresses two factors: (1) the deadening effect on innovation that results from public authorities focusing on particular pollution-control technologies and (2) the negative effects resulting when emission limitations are put on the wrong variable.

Regarding the last point, the example of Figure 14-2 shows what happens, at least conceptually, when effluent limitations are put on something like emissions per unit of input, rather than total emissions, per se. This is not to imply that this is the only way that the EPA sets emission standards. Sometimes they will establish limits on emissions per unit of output. The reason for this is that if they put limits on total emissions, they would have to face directly the plant size problem, across sources and within each source over time. They would have to track rates of output for each source and translate these into limitations on total emissions. If, instead, they express limits in terms of emissions per unit of output, they avoid this sizing problem. But it is important to point out that the technology-based emission standards approach has historically biased the overall effort towards end-of-the line pollution-control technologies.

The section on technology-based effluent standards ends with a discussion of *enforcement*. Ideas stressed are the relative ease of checking *initial* compliance, and the misplaced sense of concreteness that technology standards give to public authorities as well as the general public.

The next part of the chapter deals with the federal program of *subsidies to municipalities for constructing wastewater treatment facilities*. This has been somewhat overtaken by events now, because of the recent (1980s) shift to state revolving funds. But a discussion of the history of this program can be very instructive in discussing the perverse effects built into subsidy programs.

Finally, the chapter has a section on *new directions* in water pollution control. Considerable discussion is presented on the new effort to move in the direction of Total Maximum Daily Load (TMDL) requirements. Trading possibilities are also discussed: it contains a brief discussion on the Fox *River program* of transferable permits and *point-nonpoint source* emission trading. There has been relatively strong interest in introducing more incentive-based approaches into the FWRCA program. It remains to be seen when and if this will be accomplished.

Teaching Ideas

In discussing federal pollution-control policy there is obviously a decision that has to be made about how much descriptive detail to go into. This can be a bottomless pit if pursued with any vigor, and there is a real risk of losing analytical clarity in a morass of acronyms and program details. I have tried to avoid this by focusing only on the major features of the effort, with an analytical rather than a descriptive perspective. Of course, this means that lots of interesting elements of the federal program get short shrift, or no shrift at all. But it is a tradeoff I thought necessary in trying to boil the whole thing into a single chapter.

I have characterized the 1972 FWPCA as technology-based rather than ambient media-based. One can argue that at least the intent of the act was to be media-based, since states were supposed to get water quality goals and work back to control programs. But the federal, technology-based feature of the act quickly proceeded to overtake the state plans, so the program became, in effect, a federally mandated technology-based effluent standard approach.

Answers to Discussion Questions

1. A technology-based program is one that seeks to get polluters to adopt particular types of technologies to control their emissions, usually technologies that have been identified by regulatory authorities. A media-based approach is one where one decides how much of a total reduction in emissions one wants, usually to obtain a given target level of improvement in water quality, and then lets sources figure out themselves how to reduce emissions.

2. Clearly the extent to which TMDL targets will be reached will depend on how vigorously the equimarginal rule is pursued. In this it is no different from any other pollution-control program. Most likely the EPA, in establishing TMDLs for specific water bodies, will, either explicitly or implicitly, take costs and benefits into account, thereby achieving some degree of improvement in terms of the efficiency criterion.

3. Cost-effectiveness would suggest differential degrees of control, at least where producers of bleached and unbleached paper are contributing to a common pollution problem. One could use a diagram such as this, which is a slightly different rendition of the equimarginal principle.

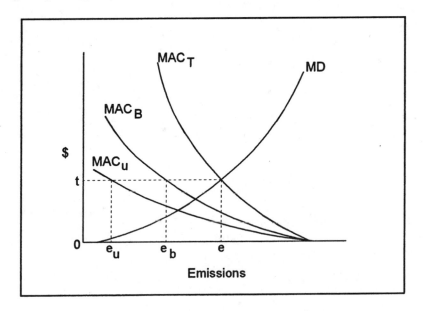

MAC_u and MAC_B are, respectively, the marginal abatement costs of the unbleached and bleached paper processes, while MAC_T is the aggregation of these two. According to the MD curve, e is the efficient level of total emissions, to be divided into e_b from the bleached paper plants and e_u from the unbleached paper sources. Possible points of discussion: If e_u and e_b are emission standards that have been achieved, the total costs of controlling emissions at the unbleached paper sources may be higher than at the others. If a common emissions tax (at level t) was levied on the sources, however, total compliance plus tax charges would be higher at the bleached than the unbleached source. If a single plant or firm contained both types of processes, and if the plant or firm was subject to a limitation of total emissions of e, it would minimize its total emission control cost by establishing the two emission levels e_u and e_b, assuming it was given the flexibility to adjust these two emission levels as it wished.

4. They are not inconsistent. Technology-based programs are usually cost-ineffective in the short run because they violate the equimarginal rule. In the long run they also can weaken the incentives for polluters to find less expensive ways of controlling emissions.

5. A media-based approach would say: "Look at the quality of the receiving waters; if you seek to improve it, require the various sources to reduce their emissions until the water quality targets are met." A technology-based approach says: "Install the specified technology to reduce your emissions, no matter what the current ambient water quality." So a combined program would specify various control technologies after having considered water quality targets and what the adoption of the technologies would achieve in terms of desired improvements.

Chapter 15

FEDERAL AIR POLLUTION-CONTROL POLICY

Objectives

The aim here is to give the same treatment to federal air pollution-control policy as the last chapter did to water-pollution policy. The chapter describes the main features of the air pollution-control program, then focuses on them with the analytical concepts discussed earlier.

Main Points

Table 15-1 gives some very aggregate numbers relative to emissions of criteria pollutants in 1970, 1980, 1990, and 1997. Again, this is a "before/after" discussion, not a "with/without," so it should be approached with caution. The numbers show modest declines for the most part, except for lead, emissions of which have been greatly reduced. Table 15-2 shows some results of the EPA's major study to assess the impact of the Clean Air Act. The next step is to sketch the recent history of federal air pollution laws. This is done in Table 15-3 and the related discussion. The section ends with a relatively extended discussion of the contents of the *1990 Clean Air Act Amendments,* both because the 1990 Act is the last major piece of environmental legislation enacted in Washington, and because it contains the interesting program for trading SO_2 discharge permits among power plants.

After a discussion of the idea of national *ambient air quality standards,* the rest of the chapter is divided into two parts, dealing with stationary sources and mobile sources of air pollutants.

The stationary-source discussion focuses on the use of *technology-based emission standards,* i.e., the same "command-and-control" (CAC) type of control that characterizes water quality programs, and in fact most environmental programs in the U.S. and the world. More economic studies have been done on the excess costs of CAC type programs in air quality than in water quality. These are summarized in Table 15-6. The next part of the stationary source discussion focuses on the emission reduction credit (ERC) *trading programs* put in place during the 1980s. Finally, there is a section on the 1990 Clean Air Act Amendments, especially on the SO_2 emission permit trading plan.

The last part of the chapter discusses the mobile-source program. Since this is done in only a few pages, it is impossible to go into any detail, so I have sought to present a few leading ideas. One of these is that the mobile-source program is an excellent example of trying to solve problems with technological fixes in the absence of behavioral changes. The reductions in emissions per car have been largely offset by increases in miles driven, thus mobile-source pollution is still a significant problem. At the limit people are looking for salvation in the emission-free vehicle, especially electric vehicles, which if successful will replace the mobile-source problem with a bigger stationary source one. The section contains a brief discussion of the zero-emission vehicle plan adopted by California as part of the 1990 CAA. Recent research (e.g., Howard Gruenspecht, in the Winter 2001 issue of RFF's *Resources*) suggests that the marginal impact of the introduction of electric vehicles will be to increase emissions, because it will cause people to hold onto older cars longer. The section includes a discussion of the *lead trading program*, and ends with some thoughts about possible incentive-based mobile-source programs.

Teaching Ideas

The text may not emphasize enough the potential problem of nonuniform emissions in the 1990 CAA transferable discharge permit (TDP) program. Permits have been awarded to power plants in many states, from New Hampshire to Georgia to Minnesota. These plants do not all contribute in the same degree to the acid rain problem the program is meant to attack. For example, one of the first trades was from a power plant in Wisconsin to one in Tennessee. In this regard see the article in the *New York Times* of March 18, 1993, p. Bl. It discusses a pending permit trade from a utility in Long Island to a coal company (to make matters worse, these permits were awarded for *past* emission reductions). If these are resold to, say, a coal-fired plant in Ohio, East Coast acid deposition could actually get worse.

Experience is now starting to accumulate on the 1990 program. Most students of the plan have been surprised at how low the permit prices have been. This is discussed in Example 15-1 and gives a good opportunity to emphasize again the point that regulators are likely to have no good way of knowing what actual marginal abatement costs are in the real world.

Answers to Discussion Questions

1. Too many permits have been given out, probably because authorities underestimated the ability of SO_2 sources to reduce their marginal abatement costs.

2. This might make a consumer automobile emissions trading program feasible. One could conceive of allotting mobile-source emission permits to people covering their annual emissions, which would be estimated at an annual inspection of their autos. Emissions in excess of their permit holdings would be subject to a stiff fine, but they would be allowed to buy and sell permits of other motorists. If they planned, or needed because of circumstances, to travel farther they could buy additional permits; if they found ways of reducing their mileage they could sell some of their permits. It is easy to point out

the problems of a scheme such as this, particularly keeping track of transactions and permit holdings of each driver, but these could probably be solved with sufficient skill and will. At any rate, a plan such as this is a good means of exploring some of the features of a transferable discharge permit program (e.g., do new drivers get permits granted to them, or must they buy into the permit market?).

3. A uniformly-applied product standard basically creates, at a cost, a product with a mandated characteristic. Anyone who would otherwise be willing to pay more for that characteristic than its actual cost gets a positive net benefit; anyone who would ordinarily be willing to pay less for it than its cost gets a negative net benefit. Rural dwellers could get the same quality of air as in an urban area at far less cost, since they chose to live in a place where there are fewer cars. By forcing rural people to buy more expensive cars with lower emissions, they maybe are being forced to "buy" cleaner air than they want. Alternatively, if the standards are efficient for the rural dwellers (set, that is, to give them the amount of clean air that they want at that cost), they are probably too lax for urban dwellers. Of course, there would be some practical difficulties with having less strict emission standards for cars sold in rural areas. One that comes to mind is that people could buy cars in rural areas, where they would be cheaper because of less stringent emissions equipment, and then transport them to urban areas.

4. New source bias refers to holding new sources to more stringent standards than existing sources. One negative incentive this creates is for people (factory owners, car owners) to hold onto their existing high-emissions equipment, rather than replace it with equipment that must meet more stringent standards. One advantage is that it may be a politically feasible way of gradually getting stricter standards adopted. An economic disadvantage is that it may be a way for existing firms to make it more costly for new firms to start up, thus sheltering themselves from potential competition. On the other hand, many people have said that it is cheaper to build pollution control into new sources as they are being built, than to retrofit existing plants; to the extent this is true, the new-source bias may be efficient.

Chapter 16

FEDERAL POLICY ON
TOXIC AND HAZARDOUS SUBSTANCES

Objectives

The objective of this chapter is to look at some of the basic economic dimensions of the very complicated system involving the use and disposal of toxic and hazardous materials. In keeping with the previous two chapters on water and air, the aim is to convey to students a relatively small number of the more important applications of economic principles to this complicated system.

Main Points

The chapter is divided into three parts: after a couple of pages of introductory remarks, it has sections on (1) the use of chemicals in production and their appearance in consumer and producer goods, (2) air and waterborne emissions of toxic materials, and (3) handling, transporting, and disposing of hazardous substances. Table 16-1 summarizes the important federal laws dealing with toxic substances, organized by these three categories.

The first section contains brief sketches of the Federal Insecticide, Fungicide and Rodenticide Act (FIFRA); the Food, Drug and Cosmetic Act (FDCA); the Toxic Substances Control Act (TSCA); and the Occupational Safety and Health Act (OSHA). Each sketch tries to convey what the act is aimed at and the mechanism by which it operates. The section discusses the general issue of *"balancing"* as it applies to chemicals in the workplace and in products. Balancing is to be contrasted with either outright prohibition on the one hand, or unconstrained use on the other. The section addresses the question of making balancing decisions in a world of costly information—information about the toxicity of tested chemicals and information about substitutes that are likely to be adopted if particular chemicals are banned or controlled. It also discusses the implicit balancing that goes on when statutes written with specific standards are enforced with costly resources.

Uniformity of standards is discussed in the next section, with an application to the control of exposure to chemicals in the workplace. The discussion brings up the question of whether the market will adjust so that wage differentials will be sufficient to compensate for differential risk. (For a longer discussion of this issue see Stephen J. K. Walters, *Enterprise, Government and the Public*, McGraw-Hill, 1993, pp. 540-546.) The role of information is stressed.

The next section addresses toxic *emissions*. After brief reviews of the toxins sections of water and air pollution control laws, and the Safe-Water Drinking Act, the discussion turns to economic issues. This focuses on waste reduction and the ways of bringing it about. The text mentions liability laws and emission taxes and stresses the role of information disclosure. By requiring firms to disclose toxins they emit, negotiations at the local level may be able to identify and move toward something approaching efficient levels of emissions.

The last section of the chapter deals with *hazardous wastes*. The policy discussion focuses on Resource Conservation and Recovery Act (RCRA) and Comprehensive Environmental Response, Compensation and Liability Act (CERCLA), offering short summaries of the content of these laws. There is also a short discussion of laws dealing with radioactive waste. As regards economic issues, the text discusses the feasibility of waste-end taxes, deposit refund systems, and the thorny problem of financing the cleaning up of old hazardous waste dump sites. This section contains a discussion of the brown fields problem.

Teaching Ideas

When it comes to chemicals and other toxic materials, students' ability to think rationally tends to fly out the window, or, rather, a different type of rationality takes over. Most students, especially those who have developed a strong environmental advocacy perspective, will approach chemicals policy with an implicit DDT-type model in mind—if a chemical offends in any way, ban it. It is difficult to get across to them the idea that, though this is indeed the efficient thing to do in many cases, a more explicit balancing perspective is appropriate in others. One has to be prepared, however, to discuss the real problems of how to have effective balancing in the real world of many chemicals, costly research, and scarce information.

Answers to Discussion Questions

1. This follows the discussion of the text. At some point a deposit would be paid on hazardous materials moving into the disposal system, perhaps by the firm making the disposal, perhaps by the handler or transporter. This deposit would then be returned when the material was delivered to a qualified hazardous-waste disposal site. One should note here the importance of testing—to avoid situations where handlers add material to their stock of hazardous waste so they can qualify for larger refunds.

2. This is the "with/without" versus "before/after" question (see the Main Points of this chapter). If the chemical responsible for the residue is banned, another is likely to be used in its place. Thus, we have to know the impacts of possible substitutes before we can draw conclusions about the health impacts of the ban.

3. The advantages include the widened liability involved, meaning that the potential pool of reimbursed cleanup funds is larger. It also provides the incentive for private firms to pursue others to get cleanup funds instead of putting the entire responsibility for this on the EPA. Disadvantages include the massive legal wrangling that goes on among potentially responsible parties.

4. A biased siting decision process, and a land market that leads to the observed pattern.

5. Attitudes toward risk will clearly affect the willingness to pay of people to reduce chemical exposure risks of varying types. It's not just a matter of making decisions according to the risk involved, e.g., risk of premature death because of exposure to arsenic in drinking water. Also involved is how people feel about this risk, especially in comparison with other risky situations.

Chapter 17

STATE AND LOCAL ENVIRONMENTAL ISSUES

Objectives

The aim here is to get students to appreciate that much in the way of environmental policy is taking place at the state and local levels, and to introduce them to the analytics of several of the programs for which the initiative comes largely at the nonfederal level.

Main Points

The chapter begins with some descriptive material on environmental expenditures in the individual states. This leads into a short section on the question of those circumstances where state action on the environment is to be preferred to federal action, from an economic as well as a constitutional point of view. A point is made that states have often been the true innovators in environmental policy; many programs enacted at the federal level have been initiated and first tried out at the level of the states.

The rest of the chapter deals with several major environmental problems where initiative rests at the state and local levels. These are municipal solid waste and recycling, land use issues, and groundwater protection.

Teaching Ideas

The states and communities are laboratories for environmental policy initiatives. They also bear important responsibilities for helping to carry out federal policy. States in particular have important roles in enforcement, because in most cases federal laws call on state and local resources to design and carry out enforcement programs. Were it not for problems of space this chapter might have included more on the economics of enforcement; this problem is beginning to receive the research attention it deserves.

The text contains a short discussion of the problem of identifying the most appropriate level of government for particular environmental problems. This offers an entry into topics of an institutional nature: the nature of organizations for collective decisions, the "match" between current collective organizations and the physical problems of the natural world, transactions costs of collective organizations, and so on.

One local and state-level issue that is currently hot is whether restrictions may be placed on solid waste shipments between localities and between states. Some communities have invested in solid waste sorting and handling facilities, in the process passing laws (called flow-control laws) that restrict where solid waste may be shipped. This is usually done in the name of assuring an adequate supply of solid waste to the local facilities. Municipalities in many states, particularly those of the Northeast, are shipping a great deal of solid waste to landfills in other states, which has prompted many people in the receiving states to seek to limit imports of solid waste from outside the state. The evolving law and politics of this are very complicated (for a good brief discussion see: Margaret A. Walls and Barbra L. Marcus, "Should Congress Allow States to Restrict Waste Imports?," in *Resources*, No. 110, Winter 1993, Resources for the Future, Washington, D.C.) but it is a good chance to discuss the cost implications of seemingly reasonable environmental laws. Most students will probably agree with the proposition that localities and states ought to be allowed to keep out solid waste from other political jurisdictions. But if these limitations are made legal (for the most part they are not now because of the interstate commerce clause of the Constitution) they will substantially increase the costs of solid waste disposal.

Answers to Discussion Questions

1. Different sectors presumably face different costs regarding what it would take to reduce their recycling ratios. Cost effectiveness would imply taking advantage of these cost differences and moving toward a situation where the marginal costs of recycling are equalized across sectors.

2. Permits could be distributed among materials users. Each permit would require the use of a certain amount of recycled material in the production process. By allowing trading, permits would be exchanged among firms that have different recycling costs, thereby moving to a situation where a given amount of recycling is accomplished with minimum cost.

3. This would essentially lower the recycled materials supply curve facing materials users, leading to an increase in the recycling ratio.

4. The main factor is whether the environmental problem is entirely contained within a community, or whether it goes across community borders. In these days of low transportation costs and substantial mobility people in one community can have preferences (willingness to pay) for environmental quality factors in other communities. Thus, the connections can be both environmental (in the physical sense) and socioeconomic.

5. Enforcement, prices charged, ability of consumers to move to lower material inputs, incomes of residents, and the presence of related programs such as a recycling program.

Chapter 18

ENVIRONMENTAL ISSUES IN
OTHER INDUSTRIALIZED COUNTRIES

Objectives

This is the first of four chapters dealing with international dimensions of environmental economics. The primary aim of this chapter is to widen students' perspectives in introducing them to the experience of other countries in terms of ambient environmental qualities, attitudes towards environmental policies, and some of the specific programs being pursued elsewhere. The objective is both to learn something about the experience of other countries and to get a better understanding of the domestic situation by comparing and contrasting it with experience elsewhere.

Main Points

The chapter begins with some comparative data on several ambient indices and on sets of emissions data. These need to be treated with caution, because they come from a variety of sources and are not necessarily based on common definitions and data-gathering practices. The next section discusses conceptually the question of comparing ambient quality levels among countries (the same considerations are relevant to comparisons among any political divisions). The point is that these comparisons have to take into account differences in assimilative capacity and economic circumstances as well as policy differences between countries. The section provides another opportunity to stress the importance of *enforcement costs*. The text contains excerpts from statements of public officials in several European countries, to the effect that there are adequate laws on the books but they are not being enforced.

The next section of this chapter discusses environmental policy experience in industrialized countries. It deals with the "style" issue, i.e., the confrontational approach to policy in the U.S. versus the more consultative approach in some other countries. The section attempts to stress the conclusion that different national styles can lead to similar results and that in the U.S. the confrontational style is not necessarily bad, but rather is just the way things are done. The section covers a brief discussion of the *polluter-pays* principle; it is important to point out that this principle has been advocated among European countries not so much because of its moral content but because of its implications for production costs and the reduction of trading subsidies. Next there is a discussion of the *European approach to emission taxes*, in which they have been relied upon primarily for revenue raising, not for inducing directly decreases in emissions.

The chapter contains a brief segment on *environmental problems in the ex-socialist countries*. This is a fascinating topic, and much more could be included if there was space. It is an eye opening lesson for students to realize that in these countries, where the profit motive was not in operation, there have been massive and serious problems of air and water pollution, worse than those of the capitalist world. The discussion traces this to the underlying incentives facing socialist firm managers. Stress needs to be put also on the nature of the political process, which made it difficult for the average sufferer of environmental externalities to seek redress through an open political process.

The chapter ends with a discussion of *environmental accounting*. This is an important new topic, but one in which main doctrines and procedures have not been sufficiently well developed as yet to warrant a larger treatment. Thus, it seemed best to present it in the context of comparing some of the approaches being undertaken in different countries. The World Bank's recent effort is discussed in Exhibit 18-2.

Teaching Ideas

Comparison and contrast is a great pedagogical approach, and students can learn much about environmental policy in their own country by looking at experience elsewhere. It's especially good for them to learn that no country is totally superior in environmental matters—that each one is struggling with its own problems, and has successes and failures. It's important to get this message across, to counter experiences like the 1992 earth summit, where U.S. policy makers, by sheer political ineptitude, created an impression of the U.S. as environmentally backward.

Answers to Discussion Questions

1. Only if marginal abatement and damage functions in the two countries were the same. Since this is hardly ever likely to prevail, similar emissions data would not imply anything about relative degrees of efficiency in the two cases.

2. The polluter-pays principle says simply that polluters themselves should be responsible for covering the costs of pollution control (rather than, e.g., the public through pollution-control subsidies). The application to nonpoint source emissions is direct.

3. The trouble with a low emissions tax is that it can create a lot of revenue only if emissions are relatively high. However, if the efficient level of emissions is not too low, a tax on these emissions may be large enough to yield a revenue large enough to cover the total costs of abating to that level. In the following diagram, suppose e' is the efficient level. A tax of t on this level of emissions yields revenues of $a, which may be enough to cover abatement costs of $b.

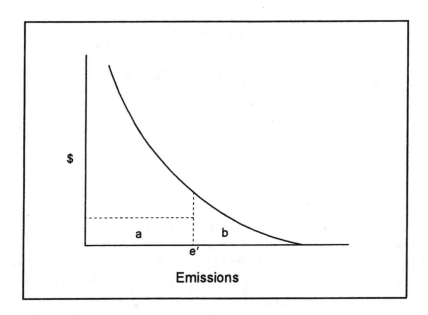

Note that this is below the necessary allocative tax that would cause the firm to reduce emissions to e'. As the efficient emissions level is reduced, the ability to do this diminishes.

4. This question refers in part to the material in the chapter on policy style. National styles and institutional histories often determine the most effective methods of procedure for people in different counties. Within the U.S., however, it is interesting to speculate about whether greater progress would be possible in some cases if we adopted less confrontational approaches and relied more on arbitration and negotiation. The early evidence on the Clinton administration would seem to suggest that they would like to move more toward negotiated policy arrangements. Much hinges on monitoring. If monitoring is difficult, people are not likely to trust parties to stick to negotiated local agreements.

5. This means expanding the national income accounts so that they properly reflect environmental degradation, as well as the standard aspects of economic activity.

Chapter 19

ECONOMIC DEVELOPMENT
AND THE ENVIRONMENT

Objectives

The aim of this chapter is to review the main economic dimensions associated with the problem of managing environmental quality in developing countries. This issue has taken center stage as a result of the Brundtland report, the 1992 earth summit, and other factors. It is all caught up in the pushing and shoving of post cold-war international political economy. The attempt in this chapter is to highlight some of the economic facets of the problem, using as much as possible the standard analytical tools presented earlier.

Main Points

The chapter begins by revisiting the distinction between positive and normative issues. Students are used to talking about these problems almost exclusively in normative terms, so an effort is made in the chapter to emphasize the positive questions that need to be addressed if environmental problems in these countries are to be effectively pursued.

The first part of the chapter deals with the differences between developing and developed countries in terms of available tradeoffs between conventional marketed goods and environmental quality. But this is a static view, and the essence of development is long-run change, so the discussion turns to the issue of *sustainability* and *long-run relationships* between development (in terms of advancing incomes) and environmental quality. The idea of sustainability was discussed in Chapter 2 with the aid of production possibility curves; this chapter adds some material taken from the World Bank (Figure 19-2) on the relation between economic growth and different environmental quality indices. The "environmental Kuznets curve," as represented by the material in Figure 19-2, has become a much more popular topic in recent years.

The pollution-haven hypothesis is discussed next. The text presents some results that are mildly consistent with the hypothesis, but the discussion emphasizes the difficulties in interpreting these data, in particular being able to determine whether the growth of dirty industries in developing countries is a result of lax environmental laws or is part of a normal developmental sequence.

The next section addresses environmental decision making in developing countries. It first takes up the issue of whether *benefit-cost analysis is* a useful decision tool for developing countries, given the often highly skewed distributions of income there, and the question of the discount rate to use in these settings. It is worth emphasizing that people can be made worse off by using discount rates that are too low, just as they can by using rates that are too high. The section also contains discussions of the well-known problem of *disincentives* that policy makers in developing countries have often put in place (though this is certainly a feature of developed countries as well), or that result from institutional factors such as property-rights regimes. The section touches on population policy as an approach to environmental quality, and ends with a discussion of whether developing countries would be better advised to opt for command-and-control or incentive-based environmental policies.

The chapter ends with a section on the roles that developed countries can play in helping developing nations deal with environmental quality issues. It discusses the issues of *technology transfer, debt-for-nature swaps,* and the use of environmentally sensitive criteria in the activities of international lending agencies.

Teaching Ideas

This book has focused on environmental economics, especially the economics of pollution control, and does not include the standard questions on natural resource economics. The distinction between these two topics is harder to sustain when it comes to developing countries. So the discussion in this chapter tends to subsume issues under both topics, e.g., soil degradation resulting from property rights problems as well as air and water pollution problems of urban areas.

The popular term for discussing the resource and environmental problems of developing countries is *sustainability*. The term has many interpretations. Economists have sought to give it rigorous analytical meaning, politicians have adopted it as a leading term in their struggle over development aid and international policy, and environmentalists have embraced it as a kind of open-sesame concept with which to reestablish future priorities.

Answers to Discussion Questions

1. One way of expressing this would be:

$$\frac{\text{Total}}{\text{Emissions}} = \frac{\text{Total Number}}{\text{of People}} \times \frac{\text{Income}}{\text{per Person}} \times \frac{\text{Emissions per}}{\text{Dollar of Income}}$$

2. If by sustainable we mean nondiminution, say from current levels, it may not be a particularly relevant guide. Reversibility implies that current generations could choose a given level of environmental quality, and future generations could choose another level, either higher or lower.

3.   Many students feel that when U.S. businesses set up operations in a developing country, they should continue to operate under U.S. environmental laws rather than the laws of the host country. Their thinking is that, if they operate under the less restrictive laws of the developing country, they are taking advantage of the people there to further their own economic ends. On the other hand, one can argue that the environmental laws of the developing countries reflect their social decisions about the desired tradeoff between environmental quality and conventional output (this of course makes a big assumption about collective choice procedures in these countries). Thus, if firms operate according to some other "terms of trade," the local population will be worse off, in terms of their own objectives, than if the firms had followed local laws.

4.   Many people argue that the institutions of public administration are relatively weak in developing countries, so "sophisticated" environmental control policies will be hard to carry out with success. For example, transferable discharge permits require that public authorities establish and oversee competitive markets for newly defined property rights, something that is proving difficult even in developed economies. These kinds of administrative difficulties argue for keeping the rules simple and straightforward, relying on standards that do not require sophisticated monitoring. At the same time, of course, developing countries cannot readily afford policies that are not reasonably cost effective. Perhaps this argues for simple emission taxes in these settings, with the proceeds to be used for helping businesses adopt more environmentally sensitive production methods.

Chapter 20

THE GLOBAL ENVIRONMENT

Objectives

This chapter contains discussions of three major global environmental issues: ozone depletion, the greenhouse effect, and the decline of biological diversity. The science underlying these problems is still uncertain and controversial. Much of the economics is still highly speculative also, both because the science is unclear and because global economic impacts are especially difficult to estimate with accuracy. Thus, the chapter aims at outlining some of the current thinking about these problems, realizing that much will change over the years as they become more fully understood.

Main Points

The chapter begins with ozone depletion, starting with a sketch of the nature of the physical problem. New scientific data on ozone depletion continue to become available; measurements in Spring 1993 show a 10-20% decline in the ozone shield over heavily populated northern mid latitudes, but there is some thought that this may be temporary, resulting from the eruption of Mt. Pinatubo in the Philippines. The next section mentions damage costs, good estimates of which are hard to find, then the discussion turns to policy response. Here the main emphasis is the *Montreal Protocol,* which is leading to a worldwide phaseout of (chlorofluorocarbons) CFCs and other ozone-destroying chemicals. The provisions of the Protocol are shown in Table 20-1, but the phaseout schedule in some countries (such as the U.S.) has been accelerated as new evidence of ozone depletion has become available. Exhibit 20-1 discusses some recent observations about the difficulty of phasing out CFC's globally.

This section ends with a discussion of some of the *economic implications of the CFC phaseout* in the U.S., which is being accomplished by a system of transferable production quotas, similar to the method used in phasing out leaded gasoline. There is not the space, unfortunately, to deal with all the interesting economic questions surrounding the CFC phaseout, such as the switchover to substitutes, the recycling of CFCs, international quota transfers, etc.

The next section of the chapter deals with global warming, the accumulation of CO_2 and other greenhouse gases in the earth's atmosphere. It follows roughly the same format, first a discussion of the scientific problem, then discussion of the problems of choice. The latter is broken into several subtopics. First we mention the issue of making choices in cases where there is scientific uncertainty but potentially very large costs if we don't respond. Then we discuss the way that CO_2 emissions are affected by changes over time in constituent factors: *population, economic development, energy efficiency, and the CO_2 content of energy inputs.* The subsection of "policy responses" contains a discussion of the differential impacts of any CO_2-limiting treaty on different countries, effects of a carbon tax on CO_2 emissions, and the possibilities of developing a system of tradable CO_2 emission permits among the countries of the world. Since the second edition, the Kyoto Protocol has come to occupy center stage. Exhibit 20-3 shows the main provisions of this agreement.

Finally, the chapter contains a discussion of the problem of preserving biological diversity. This is a very quick discussion of a large and complicated problem. The discussion emphasizes the conceptual nature of the problem, and how it differs from species preservation; it also discusses the incentive effects that lie at the root of the problem, and some thoughts reflecting recent research on possible institutional changes that would contribute to the preservation of biological diversity.

Teaching Ideas

This chapter and the next, on international environmental agreements, are perhaps best approached as a package. The present chapter outlines several of the major international environmental problems and some of the economic ramifications they entail. It discusses the Montreal Protocol and several possible policy approaches to the global greenhouse phenomenon. But one cannot talk about these issues very long before one is confronted with the question of developing international agreements and international institutions that will have sufficient power to get sovereign countries to behave appropriately, which puts the spotlight on the process of getting and enforcing agreements.

Clearly one of the biggest problems working against coming to grips with these huge global problems is the massive uncertainty involved, about the impacts on people in different countries and about the costs of taking mitigation steps. So the scientific discovery process is very much a part of the policy process, as it is in any environmental problem but perhaps even more in this case. Chief among the scientific questions are the cost estimates of shifting to lower CO_2 emissions paths; on this see Darius W. Gaskins, Jr. and John P. Weyant, "Model Comparisons of the Costs of Reducing CO_2 Emissions," *American Economic Review*, 83(2), May 1993, pp. 318-323.

The actions on ozone depletion—basically the reduction of chemicals (chiefly CFCs) that harm the ozone layer—provide a good example for the point that it is often ineffective, maybe even dangerous, to treat individual pollution problems in isolation. The relative ease with which the Montreal Protocol was signed and tightened has been driven by the development of commercial substitution, such as perfluorocarbons, which are a class of chemicals containing only carbon and fluorine, i.e., no chlorine. But it is turning out that

70

these perfluorocarbons may have significant ability to increase greenhouse forcing, and that they may have tremendously long (c. 2,000 years) atmospheric lives. So we could be trading off a solution to one problem with an exacerbation of another, which shows how important it is to treat these problems comprehensively.

Answers to Discussion Questions

1. A rational "wait-and-see" strategy would presumably outline a series of steps to be undertaken under certain contingent events. For example, a scientific program would be outlined to be pursued over the next several decades, designed gradually to reveal more of the physical nature of the problem and the likely economic and social impacts. A series of policy steps would be laid out, with specific criteria identified as to when these steps would be undertaken. In other words, instead of simply waiting for events to unfold and then looking around for policy reactions, countries would pre-commit to undertaking certain steps when scientific investigation becomes available.

2. It is obviously very difficult to foresee long-run, totally unexpected impacts such as the ones now being produced by CFCs. It should certainly alert us to the possibility that impacts may come from totally unexpected directions. One thing it strongly suggests is that we must devote greater effort to the various sciences of the earth, to develop better models and understanding of the global environment. There must also be an institutional response, so that somewhere in the public sector there is an official entity whose responsibility it is to monitor global environmental phenomena and predict outcomes of this sort. Perhaps a U.N. agency or program, similar to the U.S. Office of Technology Assessment, would be appropriate.

3. Initially, this could lead to a reduction in the local consumption of energy, in those countries instituting the tax, through energy conservation and substitution of less energy intensive goods in production and consumption. But events, especially energy consumption in other countries not instituting the tax, could change also, and in the wrong direction. If the taxing countries are significant importers of energy, reduction in world demand could lead to lower energy prices on the world market, leading to increased consumption in other countries. From a political point of view, if several countries lower substantially their CO_2 emissions, it may take away some of the incentive other countries have to enter into binding CO_2-reducing international agreements.

4. The most efficient tax is the one placed directly on the item whose consumption we wish to reduce, in this case fuels or the carbon content of fuels. This way the effects of the tax can permeate throughout the economy, and people can adjust behaviors in thousands of ways, large and small, to reduce energy consumption. The trouble with taxing certain fuel-using activities, rather than fuel itself, is that it seeks to concentrate

energy conservation in certain areas, while overlooking others. It can also set up perverse incentives which can substantially weaken the impacts of the tax. For example, if gas guzzling cars are taxed, more people will buy cars that get greater mileage. But cars getting greater mileage will be cheaper to operate, which lowers the cost to people of taking trips, which may actually lead to an increase in their annual fuel consumption. The only way to definitely avoid such outcomes is to tax the item whose consumption we wish to reduce, in this case fuels, or the carbon content of fuels.

5.   Is it easier to get parties to join an agreement before it becomes clear which ones will suffer relatively greater costs, or only after this becomes clear? Information cuts two ways. Before we know which countries will be more affected, it may be difficult to get any of them to take the overall threat seriously. But after the information becomes available, the countries who are relatively worse off will be more willing to join an agreement, while countries that are relatively better off will have less incentive to join. An international agreement is perhaps most feasible at the beginning, if countries know there will be a large global impact but not which countries will be affected the most. They may be willing to make a collective pre-commitment to help any country which later turns out to suffer a disproportionate impact from global environmental change.

6.   Reductions could be assigned on the following criteria:

a. Equal per capita consumption.
b. Equal energy consumption per unit of final output.
c. Equal percentage reduction.
d. Reduction based on marginal abatement costs.
e. Reductions based on income levels of different countries.
f. Reductions based on historical contributions to total emissions.

It's impossible in this space to detail the efficiency and equity aspects of each of these criteria. In general, developing countries have relatively low energy consumption per capita, but relatively high energy consumption per dollar of output. It's not clear whether abatement costs would be lower in low-income countries than high-income countries; arguments can be made for either conclusion. Of course, straightforward limits on consumption per capita would burden developed countries more than developing ones, because of their higher consumption levels made possible by their greater incomes.

72

Chapter 21

INTERNATIONAL ENVIRONMENTAL AGREEMENTS

Objectives

This chapter deals with some of the economic issues relative to the making of environmental agreements by groups of countries. This topic has started to become an important focus of study within environmental economics, so the aim of the chapter is to review basic concepts, introduce students to the main types of international environmental agreements, and explore some of their primary economic attributes. While institutions and policies of environmental quality are reasonably well developed domestically in many countries, this is not the case with international environmental policies, which seem to be becoming progressively more important.

Main Points

The chapter begins with a long list (Table 21-1) of international environmental and natural resource treaties that have been signed in the past. With all the publicity in recent years about the U.S. signing a CO_2 emissions treaty, endangered species treaty, and so on, it is natural for students to think that these international efforts are something new. Thus, the purpose of the discussion and list is to show them that international treaties have been part of the scene for a long time. Indeed, if all the bilateral treaties presently in effect were listed, it would take many more pages.

A section on the economics of international agreements contains two main subsections: *bilateral agreements* and *multilateral agreements*. The first uses standard marginal damage and marginal abatement costs to depict the situations of two countries, one of which creates emissions that cause damage both to itself and to the other country. The discussion is in terms of how benefits and costs are distributed and the possibilities of negotiations and perhaps side payments to achieve reductions in the polluting country based in part on damages in the other country.

The section on multilateral treaties uses a simple numerical example to show the game theoretic aspects facing individual countries when they are trying to decide whether to be part of an international agreement. The treaty can make every country better off, but individual countries may have a strong incentive to stay out and free ride. The section also includes discussion of possible side payments that might be available (trade sanctions, foreign aid) to change the game so as to reduce the temptations to free ride. It ends with a brief discussion of the potential conflict between international treaty negotiations, which will no doubt be based on treating all nations alike, and the dictates of cost effectiveness which require that the marginal abatement costs in the different countries be taken into account.

The next section of the chapter covers the issue of *international trade and the environment*. It focuses mainly on the issue of the circumstances under which trade restrictions in the name of environmental quality may be justified. Finally, the chapter (and book) ends with a discussion of international environmental treaties that have incorporated trade restrictions of one type or another. There is an analysis of the Endangered Species Act, showing the different effects of export restrictions and import restrictions.

Teaching Ideas

This chapter is something of a specialty chapter, which not all instructors will want, or have the time, to cover. Some reviewers have questioned the value of adding it to the book, but my feeling is, given the interest and attention that the Montreal Protocol has received, and the publicity given to signing international agreements at the 1992 Rio conference, it ought to be included.

Answers to Discussion Questions

1. If Country A were to adhere to the treaty, and all others do as well, its net return would be 10. If Country A were not to adhere, and others do, its net gain would be 19, for a gain of 9. But of course if all countries try to appropriate this gain, the whole thing collapses and gains for everybody are negative.

2. Preferential access to markets for goods produced in developing countries, conventional foreign aid, technical aid in pollution control or in other economic sectors, straight-forward payments in return for adopting certain environmental policies, etc.

3. Presumably Country A would be justified in putting a tariff on this item only if its production in Country B caused environmental damage also in Country A. Suppose it was air pollution going from Country B to Country A. The people in A could justify the tariff through its effects on reducing air pollution stemming from B. Of course, for this to be valid, it has to be true that the tariff will lead to reduced emissions from B, either because of reduced output in B, or the adoption there of production methods involving lower emissions. On the other hand, suppose the production in B causes "simply" a case of local air pollution that affects only people in that country and not in A. This would presumably not be sufficient justification for a tariff imposed by A on this product produced in B.

4. Only if all marginal abatement cost functions were the same in all countries subject to the standard. This is unlikely to be the case, since countries differ in terms of industrial structure, stage of development, production technology in use, and so on. A recurrent theme in the book is that uniform standards are unlikely to equalize marginal (or total) abatement costs among different sources. This is just as true when the "sources" are different countries.

5. Suppose, on the contrary, it were true that there were very effective ways of enforcing international environmental agreements, for example because the U.N. were allowed to monitor and publicize results and intervene in cases of violation. In this case countries would be much more sensitive to the economic ramifications of the treaties they would sign. At the present time they can sign very tough sounding agreements, then adjust their degree of compliance to ease their costs to what seems reasonable in their eyes. This would be far less feasible if international enforcement were possible; in this case countries would have stronger incentives to shape specific details of the agreements. This would probably make it harder to conclude agreements, though the agreements arrived at might have more overall impact.

6. This relates to question 3. Presumably it would be efficient if people in the U.S. truly suffer damages because of the dolphin killed by Mexican fishers, that is, if they would be willing to pay to have these impacts reduced. It would not be efficient if the sole reason for the import restriction were to protect the domestic tuna industry. Whether it is equitable or not depends on one's standards of equity, as well as how the restrictions on tuna imports from Mexico impacts people in different income classes. If it could be shown that the import ban seriously hurts many low-income Mexicans working in their tuna industry, one might judge it to be unfair. Perhaps the best response in this case would be to help the Mexican fishers bear some of the cost involved with shifting to methods that lower the dolphin kill.